designed and illustrated by Morris Lundin

Stories to Tell or Read Aloud

A Collection of
Folk Tales,
Legends and Myths

Selected and Arranged by

Anne Simley

Associate Professor Emeritus
Hamline University

**BURGESS
PUBLISHING
COMPANY**

426 South Sixth Street
Minneapolis 15, Minn.

Preface

This collection of folk tales, legends, and myths is in no way intended to present anything new, but rather to assemble within a few pages samples of the fine stories that are already available in our libraries. Too often we get only the children's stories and fail to realize that there are even more tales for adults. These stories have been chosen also for qualities that make them easy to recall and tell orally.

The storyteller was once an important person in the community, but gradually books became available, and in recent years, motion pictures, radio and television, and all have reduced the need for oral storytelling. So it is fortunate indeed that during the 1800's scholars became interested in the preservation of these folk tales and legends. Because of the serious meaning that is in them, as side lights on history and sociology, they have been collected seriously by learned scholars. In reading those stories that have been transcribed directly from original sources, we are aware that many versions have undergone refinements, and other changes, but we can see how they still reflect the hopes and fears, the joys and sorrows, and the characteristics of the people.

It is my hope that young people especially, will find in these tales an inspiration to pursue the subject of folklore and to gain much enjoyment from it.

May 1962   *Anne Simley*

Folklore has gained steadily in influence and scope since the early days...... The official, the missionary, the doctor, the judge, and the trader ought, therefore, all to be equipped with knowledge of the customs and beliefs of the people to whom they are sent.............Folklore is the key to understanding and sympathy with the folk around us.

A. R. Wright - English Folklore

If the Occidental learns of the life of his brother in the Orient, then the two men of tomorrow - Eastern and Western - will have developed an understanding of each other's outlook. Any development so close as this to daily life should exert a genuine influence for mutual appreciation of cultures in the days ahead.

Glenn Frank, President
University of Wisconsin, 1929

Contents

1

The Blue Rose

Maurice Baring. Reprinted by permission of the Morning Post, London.

There lived once upon a time in China a wise Emperor who had one daughter. She was remarkable for her perfect beauty, and she was as wise as she was beautiful. The Emperor was old; his son was married and had a son; he was therefore quite happy with regard to the succession to the throne, but he wished before he died to see his daughter married to someone worthy of her.

Many suitors presented themselves to the palace as soon as it became known that the Emperor was looking for a son-in-law, but when they got there they were met by the Lord Chamberlain who told them that the Emperor had decided that only the man who found and brought back the blue rose should marry his daughter. The suitors were puzzled. What was the blue rose and where was it to be found? Many at once gave up the idea, but the others set about trying to find the blue rose.

One of them - Ti-Fun-Ti - was a merchant and immensely rich. He went to the largest shop in town and said to the shop-keeper, "I want a blue rose, the best one you have."

The shop-keeper explained that he did not stock blue roses. He had red, white, pink, and yellow roses, but no blue ones. There had never been any demand for them.

"Well," said Ti-Fun-Ti, "you must get one for me. I do not care how much money it costs, but I must have a blue rose."

Another suitor was a warrior and extremely brave. He mounted his horse and taking with him a hundred archers and a thousand horsemen, he marched into the territory of the King of Five Rivers, whom he knew to be the richest king in the world and the possessor of the rarest treasures, and demanded of him the blue rose.

The King of the Five Rivers, who disliked soldiers, and had a horror of noise, physical violence and every kind of fuss (his body guard was armed with only fans and sunshades), rose from his couch, tinkled a small bell, and said to the servant who appeared, "Fetch me the blue rose."

The servant retired and returned presently bearing on a silken cushion a large sapphire which was carved so as to imitate a full-blown rose with all its petals. "This," said the King of the Five Rivers, "is the blue rose. You are welcome to it."

The warrior took it, thanked him, and went straight back to the Emperor's palace saying that he had the blue rose. He was ushered into the presence of the Emperor who, as soon as he heard the story and saw the rose, sent for his daughter and said, "This intrepid warrior has brought what he claims to be the blue rose. Has he accomplished the quest?"

The Princess took the object in her hands and after examining it a moment said, "This is not a rose at all. It is a sapphire; I have no need of precious stones." And she returned the stone to the warrior with thanks. The warrior went away in discomfiture.

The merchant hearing of the warrior's failure, was all the more eager to win the prize. He went to the shop-keeper and said, "Have you got me the blue rose? I trust you have, for if you have not, I shall most assuredly be the means of your death. My brother-in-law is chief magistrate and I am related by marriage to all the chief officials in the kingdom."

The shop-keeper turned pale and said, "Sir, give me three days and I shall procure you the rose without fail."

The merchant granted him the three days but the shop-keeper was at his wit's end as to what he should do, for he knew well that there was no such thing. For two days he did nothing but moan and wring his hands, but on the third day he said, "Wife, we are ruined."

But his wife who was a sensible woman, said, "Nonsense. If there is no such thing as a blue rose, then we must make one. Go to the chemist and get a   strong dye that will change a white rose to a blue one."

So the shop-keeper went to the chemist who gave him a liquid into which he should dip the stem of the white rose. He did as he was told and the rose turned into a beautiful blue. The shop-keeper took it at once to the merchant who went to the palace saying that he had found the blue rose.

He was ushered into the presence of the Emperor who as soon as he saw the blue rose, sent for his daughter and said, "This wealthy merchant has brought you what he claims to be the blue rose. Has he accomplished his quest?"

The Princess examined the flower a moment and said, "This is a white rose but its stalk has been dipped in a poisonous dye and it has turned blue. Were a butterfly to settle on it, it would die of the fume. Take it back. I have no need of a dyed rose." And she returned it to the merchant with her thanks.

At last all abandoned the quest except the Lord Chief Justice who was the most skillful lawyer and statesman in the country. After thinking over the matter for some months, he sent for the most famous artist in the land and said to him, "Make me a china cup. Let it be milk white in color, and perfect in shape, and paint on it a rose, a blue rose."

The artist made obeisance and withdrew, and worked for two months on the cup. When it was finished the world had never seen such a beautiful cup, so perfect and so delicate, and the rose was like a living flower picked in fairyland and floating on the surface of that rare milky porcelain. The Chief Justice gasped with surprise and pleasure when he saw it, and said to himself, "Without doubt, the blue rose is here on this cup."

So after rewarding the artist, he went to the palace and said that he had the blue rose. When the Emperor saw the cup, he sent for his daughter and said, "This eminent lawyer has brought you what he claims to be the blue rose. Has he accomplished his quest?"

The Princess examined the bowl and then said, "This bowl is the most beautiful piece of china I have ever seen. If you are kind enough to let me keep it, I shall put it aside until I receive the blue rose, for no other flower is worthy to be placed in it."

The Chief Justice thanked the Princess for accepting it and went away.

After this there was no one who ventured on the quest. But it happened that a strolling minstrel visited the kingdom. One summer evening he was playing in the twilight outside the dark wall. He sang a little song over and over and as he sang, he heard a rustle on the wall, and a slight figure in white beckoned to him. He walked along till he came to a gate, and there was someone waiting for him, and he was gently led into the shadow of a cedar tree. He understood the message of the two bright eyes. A thousand meaningless nothings were whispered in the twilight, and the hours fled swiftly. When the East began to glow, the Princess (for it was she) said it was time to go. "But," said the minstrel, "tomorrow I shall come to the palace and ask for your hand."

"Alas," said the Princess, "I would that were possible, but my father has made a foolish condition that only he may wed me who finds the blue rose."

"That is simple," said the minstrel, "I will find it." And they said good night to each other.

The next morning the minstrel went to the palace, and on his way he picked a common white rose from a wayside garden. He was ushered into the presence of the Emperor who sent for his daughter and said to her, "This penniless minstrel has brought you what he claims to be the blue rose. Has he accomplished his quest?"

The Princess took the rose in her hands and said, "Yes, this is without doubt the blue rose."

But all who were present pointed out that the rose was white and made objection.

"I think the rose is blue," said the Princess, "Perhaps you are all color blind."

The Emperor decided that if the Princess thought the rose was blue, then it was blue. For it was well known that her perception was more acute than that of anyone else in the kingdom. So the minstrel married the Princess, and they lived in a house with a garden full of white roses, and the Emperor died in peace.

2

The Devoted Friend

Arranged from an original story by Oscar Wilde.

Once upon a time there was an honest little fellow named Hans. He had a kind heart, and a funny round good-humored face, and he lived in a tiny cottage all by himself, and every day he worked in his garden. In all the country-side there was no garden so lovely as his. Flowers and herbs bloomed in their proper order as the months went by, so there were always beautiful things to look at, and pleasant odors to smell.

Little Hans had a great many friends, but the most devoted of all was big Hugh, the miller. Indeed so devoted was the rich miller to little Hans that he would never go by his garden without leaning over the wall and plucking a large nosegay, or a handful of sweet herbs, or filling his pockets with plums and cherries if it was fruit season.

"Such friends should have everything in common," the miller used to say, and little Hans felt very proud of having a friend with such noble ideas. Sometimes, indeed, the neighbors thought it strange that the rich miller never gave little Hans anything in return, though he had a hundred sacks of flour stored in his mill, and six milk cows, and a large flock of woolly sheep; but Hans never troubled his head about these things, and nothing gave him greater pleasure than to listen to all the wonderful things the miller used to say about the unselfishness of true friendship.

So little Hans worked in his garden. During the spring, the summer and the autumn he was very happy, but when winter came, and he had no flowers or fruit to bring to the market, he suffered a good deal from cold and hunger and often had to go to bed without any food except a few dried pears or some hard nuts. And he was lonely as the miller never came to see him in winter.

"There is no good in my going to see little Hans as long as the snow lasts," the miller used to say to his wife, "for when people are in trouble they want to be left alone. So I shall wait till spring comes, and then I shall pay him a visit, and he will give me a large basket of primroses, and that will make him very happy."

"You are very thoughtful about others," said his wife as she sat in her comfortable arm chair.

"But could we not ask little Hans up here?" said the miller's youngest son. "If poor Hans is in trouble, I will give him half of my porridge, and show him my white rabbit."

"What a silly boy you are," said the miller. "If Hans came here, he might get envious, and envy is a most terrible thing. I am his best friend and I will see that he is not led into temptation. Besides if he came here, he might ask me to let him have flour on credit, and that I could not do. Flour is one thing, and friendship is another. They should not be confused."

"How well you talk," said the miller's wife. "It is just like being in church."

As soon as the winter was over, the miller said to his wife that he would go down to see little Hans.

"What a good heart you have," said his wife, "You are always thinking of others, Take a big basket with you for the flowers."

"Well, good morning, little Hans," said the miller. "How have you been all winter? We often talked of you and wondered how you were getting on."

"That was kind of you," said Hans. "I was half afraid that you had forgotten me."

"Friendship never forgets," said the miller. "Bye the bye, how lovely your primroses are looking!"

"They certainly are very lovely," said Hans. "And it is lucky for me I have so many. I am going to bring them to market and buy back my wheelbarrow with the money. You see the winter was hard, and I had no money for bread, so I sold first my silver buttons, and then my silver chain, and last my wheelbarrow, but now I will get them all back."

"Hans," said the miller," I will give you my wheel-barrow. One side is gone and something is wrong with the spokes, but I will give it to you. I think generosity is the essence of friendship, and besides I have a new wheelbarrow for myself."

"Well, this is generous of you," said little Hans, "I can easily put it in repair as I have a plank of wood in the house."

"A plank of wood," said the miller. "Well, that is just what I want for the roof of my barn. There is a large hole in it, and the corn will all get wet if I don't stop it up. It is remarkable how one good action always breeds another. Now I gave you my wheelbarrow and you give me the plank. Pray get it at once and I will set to work on my barn this very day."

So Hans got the plank and the miller complained that it wasn't a very big plank so he thought he ought to have some flowers in the bargain. Now Hans had planned to sell the flowers, "But," he said, "I would rather have your good opinion than my silver buttons any day." So he filled the basket.

The next day Hans was nailing up some honeysuckle against the porch when he heard the miller calling to him. He ran down to the garden and there was the miller with a sack of flour on his back. "Dear little Hans," he said, would you mind carrying this sack of flour to market for me?"

"I am so sorry," said Hans, "but I am very busy today."

"Well, really," said the miller, "considering that I am going to give you my wheelbarrow, it is very unfriendly of you to refuse."

"Oh don't say that," cried little Hans, "I wouldn't be unfriendly for the whole world." And he ran for his cap and trudged off with the big sack on his shoulders.

It was a hot day and he was very tired, but after a long wait, he sold the sack of flour for a good price, and hurried home with the money. He was glad he did not refuse the miller who was his best friend and would give him the wheel barrow.

Early the next day the miller came for his money, but Hans was tired and was still in bed. "I like to lie in bed and listen to the birds sing for after that I can work better," he said.

"I am glad to hear that," said the miller, "for I want you to come to the mill and fix the roof for me. That isn't asking much of a friend considering I am going to give you my wheelbarrow."

So Hans worked all day and the miller came when it was finished and said, "There is no work so delightful as what one does for others."

But somehow Hans never had time to work in his garden for the miller was always coming round to send him on long errands or to get help at the mill. Sometimes he was distressed but he consoled himself that the miller was his best friend. "Besides," he said, "he is going to give me his wheelbarrow."

Now it happened that on a very wild night someone rapped at his door. There was the miller with a lantern in one hand. "Dear little Hans," cried the miller, "I am in very great trouble. My little boy has fallen off a ladder and hurt himself. It is such a bad night that it might be better if you went for the doctor instead of me. After all, I am going to give you my wheelbarrow."

"Well, certainly," said Hans, "but you must lend me your lantern."

"Oh, no, I couldn't do that," said the miller. So Hans took his warm coat and cap and started off. What a night it was! Finally after three hours he arrived at the doctor's house. He told him what had happened and the doctor got his horse and big boots and his lantern and set out with Hans trudging behind. The storm grew worse and worse and Hans couldn't see where he was going. At last he lost his way, and wandered off into the moor which was full of deep holes, and there poor Hans was drowned. His body was found next day.

Everybody went to Hans's funeral as he was so popular, and the miller was the chief mourner.

"He is a great loss to me;" said the miller, "I had as good as given him my wheelbarrow, and now I don't know what to do with it. It is in the way at home, and in such bad repair that I can't sell it. One always suffers for being generous. I will never give anything away again."

Every year students from far-away countries come to the United States to study and learn about America. Most of these have been grown men and women enrolled in our colleges and universities. In their youth they heard many stories that we all know, and they know many stories that we do not know. One summer, several years ago, a number of these foreign students gathered at Racine, Wisconsin, to talk about their homelands and to share their experiences with their American friends. They thought it would be interesting to tell some of the stories that they had heard in their own countries. They thought these folk-tales would show how all people of the world like the same things, and how Orientals are really not so much different from us. The following three folk-tales were among those told at that meeting and recorded by Arthur W. Gosling in a book called "How The Monkey Got His Short Tail, And Other Stories." They are reprinted here by permission.

How the Monkey Got His Short Tail

Gengo Suzuki ... Japan.

lived

A long, long time ago, far away in the mountains of Japan, lived an old man and his wife. Their home was only a hut with a shabby thatched roof which leaked whenever it rained. One night there came a very heavy rain-fall that soaked right through the thatch, and dripped steadily down upon the clean rush mats.

"Oh, husband," said the wife, "the dreadful roof-leak has come again! It always comes when the skies are black and the rain falls. May the blessed Sun Goddess preserve us!"

"A roof-leak is indeed dreadful," said the old man, "but Fate is Fate."

Now, outside the clay hut was a wicked wolf who sniffed and clawed at the doors which were as thin as paper. He was ravenous for his supper. When he heard the old woman say, "Oh, husband, the dreadful roof-leak has come. It always comes when the skies are black," he said to himself. "A roof leak must be a frightening animal much stronger than I am. I must not stay here."

So he turned quickly and slunk steadily away through the darkness to the stable yard. Near the stable meanwhile, trying to open the rude door, was a horse thief. It was very dark and when the thief heard the great wolf rustling around in the bamboo thicket, he thought, "Well, there is the farmer's horse. He is not in the stable after all." So as soon as he had a good chance, he jumped on the wolf's back.

"Oh, woe is me!" cried the wolf. "The roof-leak! The terrible roof-leak!" Desperately he bounded away through the rain and the darkness toward his den trying to shake the terrible creature from his back.

"This is a very strange kind of horse for a farmer to have," thought the horse thief as he clung desperately to the wolf's neck.

The wolf bounded on and on, and at last leaped over an old dry well and landed with such a jolt that the horse thief was shaken loose from his back and fell into the deep hole.

Still terrified, the wolf ran on and soon he met a monkey.

"Oh, monkey," he cried, "I have had a frightful adventure, but the Gods have protected me. I was standing near a stable in a poor farmer's yard, and a fierce roof-leak jumped on my back. He clung to my neck like a great black leech. I was almost dead. Then the blessed Gods threw him into an old well!"

Now, the wily monkey did not believe the frightened wolf's story. After all he had never heard of such a thing before. "I have never seen a roof-leak," he said. "Your tale is very extraordinary."

"Come with me," said the wolf, "and if you do not believe me, I shall show you."

Then the wolf led the monkey back to the old well in which lay the poor frightened horse thief. But it was very very dark, and nothing could be seen.

"I am sure the roof-leak is in there," said the wolf.

"I am sure it is not," said the monkey. He was a very wise old monkey, and he said, "To hear a hundred times is not so good as to see once."

Whereupon he searched the darkness of the hole with his long tail. At the bottom of the hole, the monkey's long hairy tail flopped against the horse thief's face.

"May the Gods be praised," he cried, "Here is a rope and I can climb out."

Instantly he seized the monkey's tail intending to use it to climb out of the hole to safety. The poor monkey screamed with surprise and pain. Now at last he believed the wolf's story and thought that surely he was being held by the fierce roof-leak.   He tugged and tugged until his face was as red as the lobster on the rich man's table.   But the horse thief was very strong and he held on.

"At last the monkey's tail broke in two, and since that time, the face of the monkey has been very red, and his tail has been very short.

4

Rama's Crying For The Moon

Premala Shahane . . . India.

Long ago in India, there once ruled a very powerful King. He was always kind to the poor and to anyone that was unfortunate. His subjects were very happy people. They tried to imitate their king and make everyone around them happy.

The King had one little son by the name of Rama. Now Rama was a very good little child and was never known to cry. He played all day long as contented as he could be. Even when he stumbled and fell he did not cry.

One day when he was only three years old, he was playing on the terrace in the moonlight. The moon was large and round and it was a very beautiful moonlight. It seemed to have wiped all darkness from the earth. The Prince tossed all his toys aside, forgot all about his playmates and started to play with the moon. He talked to it as if it were another child or a good friend.

When it was time for the little Prince to go to bed, his nurse came to get him. "Now it is time for little boys to go to bed," she said. "Come to the nursery."

But the little Prince began to scream. "I won't go. I don't want to go to bed. I won't go. I want the moon! Get the moon for me!" The nurse did not know what to do. She was really frightened for she had never before seen him act so, and never had he ever before so much as cried.

"Very well, then," she said, "you may stay here a little longer." Then she went to find the King and Queen.

"Oh, your Royal Highnesses," she said, "the little Prince is ill. He is crying for the moon."

The King hurriedly called the doctors and magicians of the land. And the King's subjects heard about the child's illness and they came running to the palace. They were all afraid because they knew that the little Prince was never known to cry. They brought many kinds of toys for little Rama. The King and Queen gave him their royal jewelry to play with, but the Prince would have none of it. He threw everything away from him. "I want the moon," he cried, "I want the moon."

Players in front of the palace did all sorts of funny stunts to make the Prince laugh, but he only cried louder and harder. Jugglers tried their tricks too, but they also failed to make the Prince stop crying.

At last the King took the moon of precious stones from his royal crown and gave it to the little Prince. Rama threw it to one side. The King was very unhappy. "I have one more plan," he said. "I will send messengers from one end of the land to the other to find someone to cure the Prince of this awful sickness."

So messengers were sent to the far corners of the kingdom. One day one of the messengers rode past several little girls who were laughing merrily. The messenger became angry to see them so happy.

"Do you not know that our little Prince is sad all the time and cries for the moon? Why should you laugh when he is so very ill and sad? You must stop your playing."

One little girl laughed outright when she heard what made the Prince cry and be so sad. "Why should anyone feel sorry," she said. "If the Prince cries for the moon, why doesn't someone give it to him?"

"The messenger said, "All the doctors, jugglers and magicians of this kingdom have tried to cure little Prince Rama. All have failed. How can you, a little girl, be so sure you can cure him after all these have failed?"

"I am sure I can," the little girl answered. "It is very easy."

"Well, the King told me to fetch anyone who even thinks he can help, so come with me," he said, And he lifted the little girl onto the horse's back, and took her with him to the palace.

"My King," he said when he reached the palace, "I have here a little girl who promises to cure the Prince of his crying for the moon."

"Very well," said the King, "all the others have failed so she shall try."

So the messenger took the little child to the Prince. The little girl went very boldly up to him. "Give me a mirror," she said to the nurse who stood beside him. "Within this evening the Prince is going to smile again."

So when the moon rose, the Prince was carried to the terrace. Again the moon shone as it did on the night the Prince became ill. The little girl held the mirror in front of him. He saw the moon reflected before him.

"It is the moon," he cried. "It is the moon!" He laughed and patted the mirror with his hands. "Now the moon is mine. It is so near that I can touch it. How happy I am."

The King and the Queen and their subjects were very happy again too. "Now I want to go back to my home," the little girl said.

The King wanted her to stay and live in the palace and be a companion to the little Prince, but she was a very little girl and cried for her parents, so the messengers took her back to her home.

In after years the little Prince became a very brave and kind-hearted King, and made all of his people very happy. But he often thought of the little girl who had once made him happy.

In many countries there are old stories about children's wishing for the moon. In our own United States, Thurber's "Many Moons" is a popular version of that theme. However, with the present interest in space travel, the modern child is more interested in taking a trip to the moon than in holding it in his hands.

5

The Spinning Wheel

Dan Singh ... India.

Once upon a time a gentleman lived in a grand old house. He and his wife would have been very happy were it not for one thing. For some strange reason the gentleman asked his wife to spin at least six yards of thread each day. Now his wife, who was a very kind and beautiful lady, spun so slowly that it took her all day to spin the six yards. She became very tired.

One day her husband went on a journey. Before leaving the house, he said, "Be sure that you do your spinning. When I return you must have one hundred yards spun."

The poor woman did not know what to do. She knew she could not spin as much as her husband wanted. She left the house for a walk that she might think of some way out of her troubles. When she came to a large flat stone, she sat down.

"There must be something that I can do," she sobbed. "Who can help me? Where can I go?" She rocked to and fro in her grief.

Suddenly she stopped. "I am sure I heard soft music. No one lives about. I don't see where the sound came from. It seems very near."

She thought it very strange but she thought the music came from beneath the very stone where she sat. She got up and pushed the stone aside.

"Why this is the door of a cave!" she exclaimed.
"Someone must live down there. I'll forget my troubles and
go down and see."

When she stepped down into the cave, she saw six
women all dressed in green gowns, and all spinning. One of
the women smiled at her and then spoke. "We have been
waiting for you," she said. "We are very glad that you have
come."

"Why have you been weeping?" another one asked.

Before she knew it she told that her husband had asked
her to spin six yards each day, and that she couldn't do it.
Because she couldn't, she explained, her husband was
unhappy.

The six spinning women smiled and nodded at each
other as the thread ran through their fingers.

"Invite us to your home to dinner when your husband is
at home. I think we can help you," one of the spinners said.

"I will gladly do that if you can only help me," the
woman said. "Come tomorrow night. He will be at home."

The next night when the good man came home he was
amazed to see the great preparations being carried on for
dinner. He forgot to ask his wife about the spinning. When
the dinner hour arrived, six ladies appeared at the hall door.
The man politely escorted them to dinner.

For a time the man watched the guests quietly. At last
he could keep silent no longer. "Ladies," he said, "if it is
not impolite, may I ask you how it happens that all your
mouths are turned away to one side?"

"Oh," said one of them, "it is because we are always
spin-spin-spinning."

The man jumped to his feet. "Is that the reason?
Tom! John! Harry!" he called to his servants. "Gather up
every rock, reel, and spinning wheel in the house and burn
it, at once. I will not have my wife spoil her beautiful face
with spin-spin-spinning," he said as he sat down again.

The guests smiled and nodded and held their mouths to
one side, until they were out of his sight.

And so for the rest of her days the woman lived happily.
Never again did her husband ask her to spin nor did he even
so much as mention spinning to her.

In the last one hundred years spinning wheels have been used as ornaments, but before that time, they were a necessary fixture in most homes, and young girls had to learn to spin. Folk-tales about girls who disliked spinning are found in many lands, with many variations. Sometimes they are stories about princesses and sometimes about peasant girls, but all indicate that few girls really liked to spin.

The three following tales are taken from Yes And No Stories by George and Helen Papashvily, by whose permission they are reprinted here. The Papashvilys are the authors of two other books of stories, Anything Can Happen, 1940, and Thanks to Noah, 1946, both of which are of interest to the storyteller. All of these books are published by Harper and Bros.

6

The Man Whose Trade Was Tricks

George and Helen Papashvily
. . . Russia

There was, and yet there was not, there was once a king, who like all kings, wanted to believe that he was the trickiest man in the whole world. During the day when his court stood near to applaud each word he spoke, he felt sure of this. But at night when sleep was slow, he worried.

"Is it possible," he would think to himself, "is it really possible that there might be someone who is trickier than I?"

Finally he could endure it no longer and he called his viziers together. "Go," he commanded them, "and find the trickiest man in my kingdom and bring him here before me. I will match myself against him. If he loses, he must be my slave for life."

The viziers set out and in their travels they met many clever men - such clever men in fact, that they refused to go back and match themselves against the king for no better reward than a promise that they might be slaves. The viziers grew desperate.

At last one night they came through a fertile valley bordered with thick forests into the street of a poor village. Now this village, you should know, was not poor because it was a lazy village or a stupid village. It was poor because the king owned the valley and all the forest beyond. Each year he took such a heavy rent that no matter how hard the villagers worked when harvest time came nothing was left for them but the middlings of their own wheat and a few crooked tree stumps.

But poor as the village was, they knew how to act like rich men. They called the viziers to the best supper they could cook, and afterward, for their entertainment, built a campfire and told stories.

As the evening sharpened itself to a point, the viziers noticed that one man, Shahkro, was better than all the rest at guessing riddles, and remembering poems, and describing his adventures.

"Let us see if he will go with us and match himself against the king," whispered the viziers to one another.

At first when they asked Shahkro he refused, but finally after some persuasion he said, "I will go with you, but I will go just like this. Without my cherkasska."

And exactly that way they brought him before the king.

"Sit down," the king said. "So you think you are the trickiest man in my kingdom?"

"Tricking is my trade," Shahkro answered.

"Try to trick me, then," the king commanded. "But I warn you," he added, it cannot be done for I am so tricky myself."

"I can see that, Shahkro said, "I wish I had known all this before. I would have come prepared. As it was I left in such a hurry I didn't stop for my hat or my cherkasska, to say nothing of my tools."

"What tools?"

"Why the tools I use for tricking people."

"Go and get them."

"That is not so easy. Naturally, as I am sure you know from your own experience, I can't just bundle them together as though they were something ordinary. I need wagons."

"Wagons?" said the king. "How many wagons?"

"About a hundred with a hundred horses to pull them."

"Take them from my stable but come right back."

"Certainly," Shahkro said. "With luck I should have everything loaded in five or six months."

"Five or six months!"

"I'll need to bring all my tools if I must trick you."

"Well, come back as soon as you can."

"By the way," Shahkro said when the wagons were brought and he was ready to drive off, "if I can't trick you, I know I must be your slave for the rest of my life, but just suppose I win, what then?"

"But you can't win," the king told him.

"I know I can't but suppose I did."

"Well, what do you want?"

"Something you wouldn't miss if you gave it to me."

"I agree," said the king.

Shahkro went home at a fast trot, called all the villagers together, gave them each a horse and wagon, and working side by side, they sowed and harvested a crop large enough to last them for ten years.

"At least we have this much out of it," Shahkro said, when the last load of grain came creaking into the barn. "Now bring me all the empty wineskins you can find."

When these were collected, Shahkro blew them full of air and piled them on the wagons and rode back to the palace.

The King was waiting impatiently for him in the great hall surrounded by all his nobles dressed in their richest costumes.

"Let us begin," the king said.

"I must unpack my tools," Shahkro told him.

"I will send servants to do that," the king said.

While they were waiting the king's black dog ran into the room and, noticing the stranger there, he came over and sniffed Shahkro's legs to make his acquaintance.

Shahkro bent his head and blew lightly in the dog's ear. The dog, of course, in turn licked Shahkro's ear. "This is awful news," Shahkro jumped up from his chair. "Awful! Where's my hat? Where's my coat? I beg you loan me the fastest horse in your own stable. My dear wife, whom I left well and happy yesterday, is dying."

"How do you know?" said the king.

"How does he know?" cried the court.

"Your dog, as you saw, whispered it in my ear just now."

Everyone was sorry and the King ordered the best horse in his stable saddled, a full-blooded black Arabian, and Shahkro rode away home.

He stayed there long enough to sell the horse for a good price and to buy a black donkey. Then he put the horse's saddle and bridle on the donkey and went back to town.

The king was waiting in the courtyard and when he saw Shahkro jogging along, he cried out, "Where is my horse?"

"Horse?" Shahkro said. "Horse! Oh King, have your joke at my expense. I am only a poor man. But I never thought you would do a thing like this to me. Send me home to my sick wife on a horse that changes himself back and forth to a donkey as it suits his pleasure."

"That's impossible," the king said. "I've had that horse four or five years."

"Impossible or not," Shahkro answered. "Here I am the same as I started out for home five days ago. Here is the same bridle in my hands. Here is the same black animal under me. And it's a donkey."

The king looked at the saddle and at the bridle. He ran his hand over the donkey's flank. "Well, all I can say in apology is that he never did it while I rode him. But let's forget about that. When are you going to try a trick on me?"

"Right now," Shahkro said. "Sit down. Answer me a question. You claimed you were a trickster. Did you ever use any tools?"

"No."

"Then why did you think I would. So there I tricked you once. In all these years you had your black dog, did he ever talk to you?"

"No."

"Then why did you think he would talk to me? I tricked you twice. In all the years you had your black horse did he ever turn into a donkey for you?"

"No."

"Then why should he for me? There I tricked you three times. Now pay me and I will go."

The king saw he had one last chance to redeem his reputation as a trickster so he said, "Remember for your reward I promised only what I wouldn't miss it. Now what shall it be?"

"Your head," said Shahkro.

When the king heard this he began to shake and turn so green that Shahkro took pity on him. "Wait," he said.

"I will take another reward. Because on second thought you do use your head. It keeps your hat from lying on your shoulders. Give me instead your forest and all the fields around it for my village people to use for their own."

"Certainly," said the king, and he called his viziers and sealed the agreement right there and gave it to Shahkro. "And now I don't want to keep you for I know you are eager to get home."

Shahkro went back to his village and in honor he lived there all his life. As for the king, after that he didn't have to worry any more whether or not he was the trickiest man in the world, so I suppose he slept very well. Or maybe because he was a king he found a new worry to keep him awake.

7

The Man
Who Was
Full of Fun

George and Helen Papashvily
... Russia

There was, there was, and yet there was not, there was once a man who came home from the woods one day with three rabbits of the same color and marking.

"Vanno, Vanno," complained his wife when she saw him. "What will you do with those things?"

"Make money from them," her husband replied.

She laughed at him five minutes before she went back to pickling grape leaves. Vanno put one of the little animals in a cage outside, behind the bread oven; the second he let run around the floor, and the third he tucked into his cherkassa pocket. He dressed himself to go out.

"Wife," he cautioned from the doorway, "cook a dinner of young chickens and later if I ask you how it happened, say only, 'why, the rabbit told me, of course'."

Vanno walked to a little inn not far from home, ordered a glass of tea, and sat talking with his friends as he drank it. When he was almost finished he pulled the rabbit out of his pocket. "Run home, will you," he said, "and ask my wife to cook chickens for my dinner. Young chickens, preferably, and tell her plenty too, because I'm hungry."

He set the rabbit down, and it scampered off. Vanno put a piece of sugar between his teeth and took another sip of tea. When his friends began to laugh loudly, he turned an astonished face toward them. "What's the matter?" he asked.

"You think that messenger will carry your message home?" the men at the next table asked between bursts of laughter.

"Really," Vanna exclaimed in an annoyed fashion, "I don't know why I should notice such ignorant people, but if you doubt me, step over to my house and see for yourselves."

So they went, mocking him all the way.

"Have you something to eat ready, my dear?" he asked his wife.

"Why, yes, the rabbit told me," she answered in a matter-of-fact tone, "and I cooked chickens."

"Choose a seat at the table," he invited his dumb-founded friends, "and let us eat before our meal is overdone."

As they were serving themselves, he lifted the table cloth, and sure enough there was the second rabbit on the floor nibbling a leaf of lettuce. "Thank you, Long Ears," he said. "You made unusually good time this evening."

Now nothing would do but one of the men must buy this wonderful little creature, but Vanno would not sell him. "Part with my rabbit? Indeed not! Who would run to give my wife news of me? Who would carry my messages? No! No! It's impossible. Please do not ask."

They insisted and pleaded and cajoled until at last, very reluctantly and with tears in his eyes, Vanno accepted fifty monete, and the bargain was concluded. The purchaser was so sure of the powers of his rabbit, that he immediately walked over to the next village and bet two fields of grain with his cousin that the new pet could carry a message to his wife. The rabbit, when it was set free, of course did nothing of the kind, but probably jumped away as fast as it could to the forest and lives there yet to tell its great-grandchildren that all men are fools.

The new owner's wife was more than angry when her husband came home and asked her where was the dinner of chickens for twelve guests he had ordered.

"I have only a radish and a loaf of dry bread," she said. "Twelve guests indeed on a day I bake bread!" She would answer no more questions.

The man saw that he had been tricked, and he called all his relations and they started back to punish the fellow who had deceived them. But, before they arrived, Vanno came out to meet them.

"I'm sorry about your rabbit," he explained, "but you know what animals are. The creature was trained to come here, and of course it ran right back when you let it out." And he held up the third rabbit which had been in the cage outside all the while. "It will take a few days to accustom it to your house, you know."

The angry fellow thought, of course, that this was his rabbit. "I was hasty, I admit, Vanno," he said. "There is sense in what you say, so I'll take the rabbit home again and, in a few days perhaps, it will grow to know us."

"That's the way," said Vanno. "And now to repay you and your relations for any trouble I have caused, come tonight for supper, and I will play on my magic guitar for you."

Now Vanno planned another trick with his wife. He tied a small bladder full of pig's blood around her waist. That night after they had eaten, he tuned his long necked guitar and began to play. His wife danced in time, and it was a lovely sight to see. Suddenly he pulled his dagger out and ran it through her side. She fell as if dead and bled profusely. The guests jumped up in alarm. "What have you done," they cried, "This is terrible! This is awful!"

"Fear not, gentlemen," Vanno answered. "My guitar will bring her back." He strummed tralala, tralala, and little by little his wife revived until in three minutes, she was dancing again with beauty and grace this way and that.

This time the guests almost quarrelled as to who should buy the instrument but the owner would not hear. To each sum they mentioned, he replied, "A guitar that can restore life for seventy, eighty, ninety monete? You joke to offer me that. Please say no more. I can never part with it." So he went on until at last against his will he accepted one hundred monete from the same man who bought the rabbit.

The new owner took the guitar home as fast as he could and, being eager both to show off his fine possession and to prove that he could not be fooled twice, he immediately thrust

his dagger through his wife's side. Then he began to play,
but no matter how he plucked the strings, she would not arise.
The poor woman, alas, was dead.

He called together all his cousins and together they
went back to Vanno's home. This time they did not wait for
an explanation. They seized him and tied him in a sack.
"Drown him without a word," they all agreed.

As they carried him along the road in the sack, Vanno
cried out every few minutes, "I don't want. I simply do not
want!"

It was a long way to the water and his captors grew
tired with their burden and they were hungry. They stopped
at a little inn to refresh themselves leaving Vanno tied in the
sack outside. A shepherd who had heard him calling "I don't
want! I don't want," was curious, and he came close and
whispered, "What is it? What don't you want?"

"I don't want," said Vanno. "I just don't want."

"But what?" insisted the other

"Why, to be king. There is no need of doing this
because I'll run away again. You cannot know how very dull
it is to be king and to eat from plates with a spoon, to have
roast meat and greens with chopped nuts day in and day out.
"I don't want."

"Well," said the shepherd, "personally I think it would
be fine. I have watched beasts all my life, and I would like
to have such a chance as yours. What do you say if I untie
you, let you out, give you my flock, and go in your place?"

"If you are so foolish as to want to be king and have
people bowing down to you all the time, I have nothing further
to say," said Vanno.

So, the exchange was made. The shepherd got into the
sack and Vanno called the dogs, put the crook over his
shoulder and walked away with the shepherd's herd.

When the men inside the inn had finished their supper,
they came out, picked up their burden and went on till they
came to the lake. Rowing to the very center, they threw the
sack, herder and all, into twenty feet of water, and rowed
back. "Let him learn from that!" they said and walked to
town congratulating themselves all the way.

Imagine their surprise then, when whom should they
see coming down the road, behind a fine flock of sheep, but
the very man they had just drowned.

"Thank you," he called when he caught sight of them. "Really, let me buy you some present for all you have done for me - a skin of wine perhaps. Truly I can never repay you. I had my choice of many others but I finally took these."

"What do you mean, your choice? Where did you get that flock? We threw you in the water not ten minutes ago."

"Of course," Vanno answered, "and I found the most wonderful farm there at the bottom of the lake. You can have buffaloes, goats, cows, chickens - whatever you want for the asking. I even saw camels. Aren't my sheep fine? And I owe it all to you."

These men had been fooled once with the rabbit, and again with the guitar, but this time they thought the fellow must certainly be telling the truth. With their own hands, they had thrown him into the lake and yet, here he was, dry as flour, with a hundred animals to prove his story. "Let us try too," they said among themselves, "for we are more deserving than he is."

"I'll be glad to ferry you out to the best place to go in," offered Vanno, "for I really feel indebted to you."

They accepted and he rowed them out to the center of the lake. One after another they jumped over the side of the boat to sink or swim as best they could. And Vanno went back to town whistling all the way, for he was a man who was full of fun.

8

The Man Who Had a Good Wife

George and Helen Papashvily
. . . Russia

There was, there was, and yet there was not, there was once a man who was very lazy. When spring came, his wife said to him, "My darling, here is the grain and here is the plow and here is the ox all harnessed. Please sow our field."

By her coaxing and pleading day after day their wheat was finally planted. Then the man was so tired, he rested all summer.

When harvest time drew near his wife said, "My darling, here is the sickle and here is the whetstone. Please cut our wheat."

The first day he had an errand; the second day he was sick; the third day it looked like rain; the fourth day visitors came, but finally on the fifth day he went to the field. As soon as he saw how thick his wheat had grown, he sat down under a tree in despair. In a few minutes his wife came out.

"My darling," she said, "start cutting a little corner and by the time you have finished that I will bring you your breakfast. Then you can cut a bit more and it will be lunch. Little by little you will finish."

She went in the house and cooked him potato soup with butter and took it to him. Her husband was standing by the edge of the field cursing the crop. "Why did you have to grow so well and make me all this trouble?"

"My darling," his wife said, "eat some soup and then you will feel like starting your work."

Finally she succeeded in getting him into the field and then she went home. But from her window she could see him standing like a stone, his sickle idle in his hand. She covered her fire, closed the door and walked to her parent's house. "Lend me my brother's horse," she said, "and his suit of black clothes."

She dressed herself, put a mask over her face, and mounting her horse, went by a back way to her husband's field.

"I am the Devi whose name is Plague of the Lazy," she screamed, riding up at a furious pace. "Take that and that." She cracked him with her crop. "I go now to kill a man in the next village who wouldn't shell his corn. If your field is not finished when I pass on my way back, I will kill you too."

She gave him another slash and rode away to her parent's house where she put her brother's clothes carefully in the chest and returned to the horse to its stable. Then she went home and cooked green beans with beaten eggs for her husband's dinner and carried the pot to the field.

"My darling, here is your lunch," she called.

"I can't stop now," he said. He was throwing his sickle so fast the blade hummed. "I can't waste time. Break off food and put it in my mouth as I swing."

That way he kept on all day and by supper their crop was harvested and ready to thresh. Her husband came home, sat down and put his head between his hands. "Order my coffin," he said.

"Why?" she asked.

"Because I'm going to die."

"My darling," she said, "you are tired now, but by tomorrow you will feel rested again."

No, he wouldn't hear of this. He had made up his mind to die and nothing could stop him. He sent for a coffin; his friends came; the priest prayed; and finally the pall-bearers with tears on their faces carried him to church to lie all night at the altar before they buried him next day.

His wife waited until the mourners slept, then she went to the church door and in a great voice cried out, "All the old

and new corpses get up! It is time to begin your tasks.
Tonight the old corpses will carry one hundred bricks to
heaven; the new corpses a thousand."

When her husband heard this, he jumped from his bier,
knocked over the candles and ran all the way home. After
that he was the most industrious man in the whole village.
"For," he explained, "if I must work, isn't it better to cut
wheat alive than haul bricks dead?"

His wife said, "My darling, as always, you are quite
right."

Note: A Devi is a Goddess.
Pronunciation: it rhymes with navy.

The following three stories were found in a collection made between 1850 and 1860 in Norway by Asbjornsen and Moe, and printed in a book entitled Norske Folke Eventyr. Mr. Asbjornsen stated in a foreword that both adults and children love folk tales because in them they can see their own hopes and fears, and they will love them as long as they keep their sanity and their health. The tales perhaps originated in the East, but the story-teller using his own style, gradually reflected the imagination and the characteristics of his own people. Translation by Anne Simley.

9

Peter, Paul and Esben-Ash-lad

There was once a man who had three sons, Peter, Paul, and Esben the Ash-lad, but that is all that he had for he was so poor that he owned not even the clothes on his back. So he said that the boys would have to go out into the world to earn their own living or they would all starve.

Not far away was the palace of the King, and nearby there stood a great oak tree which cut off the light from the buildings. The King had offered much money to anyone who could cut down the tree, but no one had succeeded because for every chip that flew out, two grew back in. The King also wanted a well, - one that would hold water a whole year. All his subjects had wells but not he. To the one who could chop down the tree and dig the well, the King promised money and much more. So far no one could do the job because the castle grounds were high on a hill and a few feet down there was solid rock. So he had no luck.

But finally the King made up his mind to get the work done. He invited everyone who could chop and dig to come, and to the one who did the job he promised the Princess and half his kingdom. Many men wanted to try but the old oak tree became thicker and thicker with each blow of the axe and they couldn't dig through the rock. Finally the three brothers decided to try also. The father

agreed because he thought that if they failed to get the
Princess and the Kingdom, at least they might get work as
servants.

So they set out, and soon they came to a fir-covered
hillside, and near-by was a heath. There they heard someone chopping and chopping. "I wonder what that is chopping
up there." said Esben Ash-lad. "You are always so smart
with your wondering," said the brothers. "That is surely
something to wonder about. That is a man cutting wood."

It would be fun to see anyway," said Esben, and went
up the hill. The brothers called after him and made fun of
him, but he paid no attention. Upon the hill he saw an axe
that stood and chopped and chopped at a log.

"Good day," said Esben Ash-lad, "so you stand here
and chop, eh?"

"Yes, I've been standing here and chopping for a long
time and waiting for you," said the axe. "Well, here I am,"
said Esben, and took the axe and put it in his knapsack.

When he joined his brothers, they laughed at him.
"Well, what did you see up there on the hill?"

"Oh, it was only an axe that we heard," said Esben.

When they had travelled a little further, they came to
a plateau. They heard something there digging and drilling.
"I wonder what it is back there that drills and digs," said
Esben Ash-lad. "Well, you are so smart to guess," said the
brothers. "Maybe it is the woodpeckers on the trees that you
hear."

"Yes, but it would be fun to see what it is anyway."
And they ridiculed him but he went and when he got there
he found a spade that was digging. "Good day," he said.
"Are you standing here alone and digging?"

"Yes, I am," said the spade. "I've stood here a long
time digging, waiting for you."

"Well, here I am," said the Ash-lad. And he took the
spade and hid it in his knapsack and went to join his brothers.

"That must have been something amusing up there,"
they laughed. "Oh, it was only a spade we heard," he said.

So they went on further together until they came to a
little brook. They were all very thirsty after walking so far
so they sat down and drank. "I wonder where this water
comes from," said Esben Ash-lad. "I wonder if you are

really right in your head," said Peter and Paul. "Aren't you
a little crazy? Haven't you ever seen water gushing up out of
the ground?"

"Yes," said Esben, "but I'd like to see where it is
coming from anyway." So he went up the hill as his brothers
shouted taunts after him and laughed.

As he went up the hill, the stream became smaller and
soon he saw a huge walnut from which the water was trickling
out.

"Good day," said Esben again. "Are you lying here,
trickling and flowing all alone?"

"Yes," said the walnut, "I've been lying here trickling
and flowing for a long time waiting for you." "Well, I am
here," said Esben, and took a bit of moss and stuffed it into
the hole so the water couldn't come out. Then he put the
walnut into his knapsack and joined his brothers. "So you
found out where the water came from," they said. "It must
have been quite unusual."

"Oh, it was a hole it came out of," said Esben, and they
laughed at him. "But it was fun to see it anyway," he said.

Finally they came to the King's grounds. So many had
heard about the offer of the Princess and half the kingdom
that the oak tree was about doubled in size, for two chips
grew in for each one chopped out, you'll remember. So the
King said that from now on whoever tried and failed would
be set out on an island and both his ears would be cut off.
But that didn't scare the brothers who were certain they
could chop down the tree. So Peter tried first but it went
with him the same as with the others. They cut off his ears
and he was set out on the island. Then Paul tried, only to
meet with the same fate.

So now Esben wanted to try but the King said, "If you
want to be a sheep and follow the other two, we will cut your
ears off before you try, and save you the trouble." "Well, it
would be fun to try anyway," said Esben. So he took the axe
from his sack. "Now you chop," he said, and the axe did
chop and the chips flew, and soon the oak was down. When
that was done he took out the spade. "Now dig," he said, and
the spade dug so that the dirt and stones flew and soon there
was a well, Then he took the walnut and laid it in one corner
of the well, and he took the moss out of the hole. "Trickle

and flow, " he commanded.   And the water began to flow and
to gush out of the hole.   Soon the well was full.   And since
the ash-lad had chopped down the tree and had dug a well, he
got the Princess and half the kingdom as the King had
promised.   Maybe it was a good thing that Peter and Paul
had lost their ears or they would forever have had to hear
that Esben Ash-lad hadn't wondered in vain.

*The ash-lad appears as a hero in several old
tales.   He is usually the youngest boy, and is looked
down upon by his brothers and parents.   He is
usually a dreamer who is always poking in the ashes
of the fireplace.   Like Cinderella,   he wins out in
the end.*

10

The Mill That Grinds On The Bottom of The Sea

Once a long, long time ago there were two brothers; one was rich and the other was poor. When Christmas eve came, the poor brother had neither porridge nor bread, so he went to his rich brother and asked for a little food for Christmas in God's name. It wasn't the first time the rich brother had given him food. He was never glad to do it, nor was he now. "If you will do what I tell you to do, I will give you a whole ham," said the rich one. So the poor man promised and thanked him. "Now you have it, and you can go straight to the Devil," said the rich brother as he threw the meat at him. "Yes, I promised and so I shall have to go," said the other and he took the ham and went.

He walked all day and at dusk he came to a place all lighted up. This must be the place, he thought. In the woodshed there stood an old man with a long white beard, chopping wood for the Christmas fire.

"Good evening," said the man with the ham. "Good evening to you," said the other. "Where are you going so late?" "Well, I am going to the Devil if I am on the right road," said the poor man. "You are on the right road all right, for it is here," said the old man. "When you go in, they will all want to buy that ham, for ham is seldom served here, but you must not sell it unless you get in return the hand mill that stands behind the door. When you come out again, I'll teach you how to stop the mill which is good for all sorts of things." The man with the ham thanked him and knocked at the Devil's door.

When he went in, it happened just as the old man said. All the devils both big and little, swarmed around him like ants and each outbid the other for the ham. "Well, my wife and I had planned to have it for Christmas but since you are so determined to get it, I'll have to let you have it. But if I sell it I want in return the handmill that stands behind the door there."

That the Devil didn't want to give him so he haggled and bargained but the man was determined so finally he got the mill. When the poor man again came out into the yard, he asked the woodchopper how to stop the mill, and having learned that, thanked him, and went home as fast as he could but still he did not reach home until the clock struck twelve on Christmas eve.

"Where in the world have you been?" said his wife. "Here I have been sitting hour in and hour out waiting and hoping and not so much as two sticks to lay in a cross for a fire under the Christmas porridge."

"Well, I couldn't come sooner because I had a little of everything to fetch and a long way to go too. But now you shall see." And he put the mill on the table and bade it first grind out candles and then a tablecloth and then food and drink and all sorts of good things for Christmas. Whatever he demanded the mill ground out. The old woman crossed herself again and again and wanted to know where he got the mill but he wouldn't tell that. "That doesn't make any difference," he said, "and the mill stream never freezes over."

Then he went on grinding out food and drink and all sorts of good things and on the third day he invited his friends for a big feast.

When the rich brother saw all this he became both angry and envious. "Christmas eve he was so poor that he came to me begging for food, and now he is giving a feast as if he were a king," said he. "Where did you get all these riches?" he asked the brother. "Oh, behind the door," said the other who felt no need to give an account of himself. But later in the evening when he had eaten and drunk too much, he became a bit light headed so he brought out the mill. "This is what has given me all these riches," he said, and ordered the mill to grind out this and that. Of course, when the rich brother saw that, he wanted it and offered to pay three hundred pieces of silver for it. Finally the younger said that after haying time he would sell it, for by that time he would have enough supplies to last him for years. You may be sure the mill had no chance to get rusty in the meantime. So after haying, the older brother got the mill but the younger had been careful not to tell him how to stop it.

The morning after he brought the mill home, the rich brother sent his wife to check on the harvest hands, while he got lunch ready. When it was time he set the mill on the table and said, "Now grind out herring and porridge and quick too." So the mill ground out enough to fill all the dishes and soon the whole kitchen was full. The man became frightened because he couldn't stop the mill. Soon the whole house was full and he got out just in time to escape drowning. But the mill kept on grinding and as he fled down the road, the stream of porridge followed him.

The wife thought it was strange that he did not call her and the workmen to lunch. "I had better go and help him," she said. But when they got over the hill they saw all the herring, porridge and bread pouring out and the husband in the lead, running as if the very devil were chasing him. He was running to his brother's house to beg him to take back the mill at once, because he said, "If it grinds one more hour, the whole village will be buried." The younger wouldn't take it back until he was paid three hundred more pieces of silver.

Now the younger had both the mill and the money, so soon he bought a fine farm more grand than his brother's, and the mill ground out gold and clothes and food. He lived near the sea and his fine house shone so it was visible far out on the ocean. Everyone who saw it wanted to visit him and see the mill that they had heard about.

Finally there came a skipper who wanted to buy the mill if it could grind out salt. "Yes, it can," said the owner. So the skipper was willing to pay any price to get it so he wouldn't have to sail so far to get his cargo of salt. The owner was reluctant but eventually he let it go for a thousand pieces of silver. When the skipper got the mill he was in a great hurry to get away before the man might change his mind so he did not stop to find out how to shut it off. When he got to the ship he said, "Now grind out salt both fast and well," and the mill fairly spouted out the salt. When the ship was full, he wanted to stop the flow but he couldn't so the salt piled higher and higher and finally it sank the ship. So there is the mill at the bottom of the ocean still grinding away day in and day out, and that is the reason the sea is salt, they say.

11

Lord Peter

The trolls were characters that appear often in Scandinavian myths. They were sometimes dwarfs and sometimes giants. They were believed to live underground in caves.

Once there was a very poor couple who had almost nothing except three sons. When they died there was not much for the sons to inherit. The oldest boy took the kettle as he thought that was the best thing. The second took the griddle because he hoped that if someone borrowed it, some food would come back with it when it was returned. When the youngest, Peter, had his turn there was nothing left to choose, so he took the cat because he couldn't bear to leave her behind.

Then the brothers went each his own way, out into the world to try their luck. After Peter had gone a little way, the cat spoke to him and said, "You will be rewarded because you didn't leave me behind to starve. I shall go out into the woods and get some fine animals, and you shall take them to the palace that you see over there and tell the King that you have a present for him. If he asks who sent them you tell him that Lord Peter sent them."

Well, it wasn't long before the cat came back with a reindeer. She had sprung onto the deer's head and said, "You go to the King's palace or I'll scratch your eyes out," and the reindeer didn't dare do anything but obey. So Peter led the deer into the King's kitchen and said, "I come with a present for the King if he will accept it." When the King saw it, he was pleased with the fine

looking animal and said, "My good friend, who sent this
wonderful present?"

"Oh, it came from Lord Peter," said the boy.

"Lord Peter? Where does he live?" said the King.
But the boy said he didn't dare tell, so the King gave him
some money and told him to thank his master.

The second day the cat went again into the woods and
sprang onto the head of a great stag, and again Peter directed
the animal to the King's kitchen. He said this was another
present, and the King was even happier with the stag than
with the deer. Again he asked who had sent it, and again
Peter said he could not tell. So the King gave him some
money and he went home.

The third day the cat came with a moose. When Peter
came to the palace kitchen with this gift, the King was still
more pleased and gave Peter much more money. But he
said that since he couldn't go to see Lord Peter, would the
boy ask his master to come to see him. Peter said he would
tell him.

When the boy told the cat she said, "I was expecting
that. In three days you'll have a horse and wagon and some
fine clothes and plenty of money and you can go to see the
King. But whatever you see in the King's palace, you must
say that you have a better one at home. Peter promised and
sure enough, in three days all the clothes and the horse and
wagon were there, and everything was elegant. Peter set
out and the cat ran alongside. The King was very gracious
to Peter but no matter what he showed him, Peter said what
he had at home was better. After while the King became
angry. "I'm going home with you to see for myself," he
said, "and if you are lying, God help you!"

"Now," said Peter to the cat, "you have got me into
trouble. Now the King wants to come home with me and you
know my home is nothing."

"Oh, don't worry," said the cat, and ran on ahead.
The King and his servants followed. A short way ahead they
came to a fine flock of sheep with wool so long that it touched
the ground.

"If you will say that the sheep belong to Lord Peter,
should the King ask you, I'll give you this silver spoon,"
said the cat to the shepherd. Yes, he would do that. "Well,"
said the King when he came, "I never saw such a fine flock
of sheep. Who owns them?" "Lord Peter," said the
shepherd.

A little later they came to a grand herd of cattle. The cat ran ahead and said to the girl who herded them, "If the King comes by and asks you whose cows these are, say 'Lord Peter' and I'll give you this silver dish." She had taken the silver from the palace. The girl agreed and when the King came he was astonished to see such beautiful sleek cattle, and asked who owned them. "Lord Peter," said the girl.

So they went on and soon they came to some beautiful horses. The same thing happened there. After some time they came to a castle with one gate of silver and one of gold. The castle itself was of silver. They went in and the cat told Peter to say that this was his home. Inside it was even more lovely than outside. Everything was of gold. Well, the King had to admit that this was better than his castle. He accepted an invitation to stay for dinner, but he was plainly unhappy.

Now this castle belonged to a troll who came home while they were eating and pounded on the gate. "Who is eating my food and drinking my ale," he screamed. The cat ran out to the gate and said, "Wait a bit and I'll tell you how the peasants conduct themselves when you are away. They drive out to the fields, scatter fertilizer, seed, plow and gather crops, and then they come home, and that takes them from dawn to dusk." Knowing that Trolls can't stand the sun, the cat then said, "Turn around and you will see a lovely maiden behind you."

The Troll turned around and saw the brilliant sun. It sent out shafts of bright light and that the Troll couldn't stand, so that was the end of him.

"Now this is all yours," said the cat to Lord Peter. "Now chop my head off. That is the least you can do for me after all that I have done for you." "No, that I can't do," said Peter. "If you don't, I'll claw your eyes out," said the cat. Peter then felt he had to do it, though he did not want to. But immediately there was a beautiful Princess standing before him. "All this elegance was mine once," said the Princess, "But the Troll put a hex on me so I had to be a cat and live at your parent's home. Now you may take me as your queen if you wish for you are now King of the realm."

Of course Peter wanted her as his queen so there was a wedding very soon, you may be sure.

The following old Chippewa Indian legend was recorded by the Reverend John C. Thomas and given to my father in 1910 at the Odanah Indian Reservation in Wisconsin. The text here has been condensed but the spirit of the legend remains the same.

Leland R. Cooper
Hamline University

12

Why An Indian Woman Is Called A Squaw

When Keshamonedoo (Ke-sha-mon-e-doo) made the red man, he made him happy. The men were larger, were fleeter on foot, were more dexterous in games, and lived to an older age than now. The forest abounded with game, the trees were loaded with fruit, and birds that now have a black plumage were dressed in pure white. The birds and fowls ate no flesh, for the wide praries were covered with fruits and vegetables. The fish in the waters were large. The Munedoo (mu-ne-doo) from Heaven watched the blaze from the wigwam's fires, and these were as countless as the stars in the skies. Strange visitors from Heaven descended every few days, and inquired of the Indians whether anything was wrong. Finding them happy and contented, they returned to their high homes. These were tutelar gods, or guardians, as we would say, and they consulted with the sages of the different villages and advised them not to climb a certain vine which grew on the earth. The top of this vine reached the sky as it was a ladder on which the spirits descended from Heaven to earth to bless the red man. One of these errand-spirits became well acquainted with one of the young braves who dwelt in a cabin with his grand-mother, and extended to him an invitation to go for a stroll among the various villages around. Now

seen her only a few times and had not had the opportunity. But she lived at Echo Bay and was to be the bridesmaid, which was another reason why he skated as swiftly as the wind, and now and then shouted with exhilaration.

The drawback was that Marie's father had money, and Marie lived in a fine house and wore otter skin jackets and satin-lined mink boots when she went sledding. These things made it almost impossible for Ralph to say anything more than "I love you," but that much he intended to say no matter what came of it.

This determination grew on him as he sped along under the starlight. Venus, the love star, made a path to the west, but he had to turn his back on it and face northeast. Suddenly he felt he was not alone. His eyelashes were frosted and he thought maybe it was an illusion but he rubbed his eyes and there he saw a tall white skater in fluttering garments who sped over the ice fast as ever a werewolf went. He called out but there was no answer. However fast he went, the skater went faster. After a while he was convinced as he glanced at the North Star, that the white skater was leading him out of his direct path. He wondered if he should not keep to his road, but his companion seemed to draw him irresistibly so he followed.

Of course it came to him that this was no earthly guide. Up in those latitudes men see strange things in winter. His folks who lived on Lake Superior had told eerie tales. So Hagedorn followed the white skater all night and when the ice flushed red at dawn, and arrows of lovely light shot up into the cold heavens, she was gone and Hagedorn was at his destination. As he took off his skates, he happened to look lakeward and saw a great open place where waves showed blue as sapphires beside the gleaming ice. Had he gone along his intended path, watching the stars to guide him, his glance upwards, and at such speed, he would certainly have gone into that cold grave. The white skater had been his guardian angel!

Much impressed he went to his friend's house expecting to find all the pleasant furore of a wedding. But instead someone met him with a solemn face.

"Is this your wedding face?" said Hagedorn.

"There's no wedding today," said his friend. "Marie died last night."

"Marie--"

"Yes, she died last night. She had been skating in the afternoon, and came home chilled and wandering in her mind, and all the time she talked of you. We wondered what it meant. We did not know that you were lovers, but she said that you were on the lake and that you did not know the ice was breaking up. She cried that you could come in by the old French Creek if you only knew--."

"I did come in that way," interrupted Hagedorn.

"How did you come to do that? It is out of your way."

So Hagedorn told him how it came to pass. That day they watched beside the maiden and the bride-to-be said prayers for her friend. Then they buried her in her brides-maid's white, and Hagedorn was at the altar with her but not as he had intended. The next day her friends were married and they laid their bridal wreaths on her grave. Three nights later Hagedorn left for home. They wanted him to go by sunlight but he had his way and went when Venus made her bright path on the ice. He hoped to see the white skater but his only companion was the wind, and the only voice he heard was the baying of a wolf on the North Shore.

14

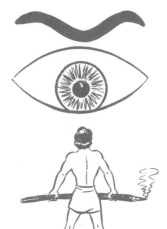

Ulysses and the Cyclops

Arranged from *Stories from the Classics*, by Eva March Tappan, Copyright 1907, Houghton, Mifflin Co.

After the fall of Troy, Ulysses set out for home, but he was destined to encounter many troubles before reaching it.

One day he and his men came to a land where the lotus grows. Now, whoever eats of the fruit forgets about loved ones and country. The Lotus-eaters did not mean to do harm, but instead meant to be kind to their guests when they gave them the fruit. After the sailors had eaten, they did not care to sail over the seas anymore, so Ulysses had to bind them and carry them to the ships.

The wind had died down which made it necessary for the sailors to row for many days. Finally they came to the land of the cyclops. About a mile from shore there was an island with a good harbor where a ship could be safe from storms. On the island were trees and clear water, and there the weary sailors slept and waited for morning. When dawn came, they explored the island and found sheep and goats and fruit so there was food for a feast. Next day Ulysses left most of his men there, but took many others and set sail for another island. That was where the cyclops lived all alone in a great cave, - a creature without law. With twelve men, Ulysses went up from the ship, taking a goat skin full of wine which the priest of Apollo had given him for protecting his family. This was

very special wine and he planned to bargain with it. Entering
the cave, they decided it must be the dwelling of some rich
shepherd, for there were pens of sheep and goats and much
cheese and milk. The sailors wanted to take the food and
leave but Ulysses wanted to stay and see what sort of person
lived there.

It was evening when the cyclops came home. He was a
mighty giant with one eye only, in the middle of his forehead.
He carried a bundle of pine logs which he threw down outside
the cave, drove his flocks in, and rolled a huge rock into the
entrance to close it. Then he milked the goats, and kindled
a fire which lighted up the cave so well that the men were
discovered hiding there.

"Who are you?" said Polyphemus, for that was the name
of the cyclops. "Are you traders or pirates?"

"We are no pirates, mighty sir," Ulysses answered.
"We are Greeks sailing back from Troy, and we are come to
beg hospitality in the name of Zeus."

"Don't talk to me of Zeus," said Polyphemus. "We
cyclops take no account of gods because we are stronger than
any of them. Where did you leave your ships?"

"Ships we have none," answered Ulysses, "for what
was ours King Neptune wrecked and we alone have escaped."

The cyclops said nothing, but with one swoop caught up
two men, dashed them on the ground, tore them limb from
limb, and ate them. After his feast of human flesh, and milk
from his goats, he went to sleep. The men could only pray
to Zeus and wait and wonder.

Ulysses pondered whether he should try to slay the huge
giant, but decided against that because they could not roll
away the great stone. So all night they waited in terror.

In the morning the cyclops seized two more men and
devoured them. Then he went to the pasture with his flock
but took care to roll the rock before the entrance to the cave.
All day Ulysses planned his escape. He cut a piece off a big
staff he found there, and sharpened it to a point in the fire
and hid it.

When the giant came home, he again drove the flock
into the cave and took two more men for his supper. Ulysses
then offered him the wine skin saying, "Drink, Polyphemus,
now that thou hast feasted. Drink and see what precious
things we had in our ship."

So the cyclops drank, and was pleased and said, "Give me again to drink and tell me your name that I may give you a gift. We have vines, but they don't bear wine like this which must be such as the Gods drink in heaven."

Ulysses gave him more wine and he drank, and he gave him even a third time knowing how it would affect his brain. Then he said, "You asked my name. It is No Man, and now give me your gift."

The giant said, "My gift is that I shall eat you last." Then he fell into a drunken sleep. Ulysses then thrust the pointed olive-wood staff into the fire till it was about to burst into flames and then thrust it into the cyclop's one eye. It hissed like hot iron in water. The giant screamed so that his neighbor cyclops came to ask the cause. He answered, "No Man slays me by craft. "Well," they said, "if no man does wrong, pray to Neptune for help."

Then the cyclops rolled away the great stone so he could sit by the entrance and catch the men if they tried to escape.

Ulysses planned what to do. He tied his six remaining men under the bellies of six rams. He put one ram on either side so they would walk out in threes. Then he clung to the under side of the biggest one, and when morning came, the rams rushed out to pasture. The cyclops was at the door and felt each as it went by, but did not think of what might be underneath. Last of all was the big ram.

"How is this," said Polyphemus, "that you are the leader of the flock but lag behind? You have always been first. Maybe you are troubled about your master's eye which some wretch has destroyed. I shall find him and avenge myself." And with that the ram passed out of the cave. When Ulysses was safely out of reach of the giant, he unloosed his comrades, and they drove the flock before them to the ship. At a safe distance out at sea, Ulysses called back "You are punished for devouring your guests. May you suffer a worse fate." The cyclops, very angry, broke off the top of a hill and hurled it, but the sailors rowed with all their might and escaped. Ulysses called again then and said, "If any man asks who blinded you, say it was Ulysses, the son of Laertes, dwelling in Ithaca."

55

15

The
Miraculous
Pitcher

Adapted from *Stories from Ovid*, (43 B.C.—18 A.D.), by Nathanial Hawthorne.

One evening in times long ago, old Philemon and his old wife Baucis were sitting at their cottage door enjoying the sunset. Rude shouts of children and barking of dogs in the village near by grew louder so that they could hardly hear each other speak. "Oh wife," cried Philemon, "I hear some poor traveler is seeking hospitality among our neighbors yonder, and instead of giving him food and lodging, they have set the dogs at him as is their custom. Some terrible thing might happen to them unless they change their ways. But as for you and me, so long as we have a crust of bread, we shall share it with any homeless stranger who needs it."

These people were quite poor but very kind and cheerful. Their cottage stood on rising ground a short distance from a village which lay in a valley. When the world was new this had been a lake, but now it was a fertile, fruitful valley. But the people were selfish and hard hearted. True they treated rich visitors very nicely, but that was not because they were kind.

So as the noise came nearer to the old couple's cottage, they could see two men humbly dressed, trying to fight off the dogs.

"Let us go to meet these poor people," said Philemon.

"You go," said Baucis. "I shall go indoors to see what I can find for supper for them."

"Welcome," said Philemon in a tone so warm and hearty that they knew he meant it. "I hope I can make amends for the inhospitality of my neighbors."

"Well said, old father," cried the traveler, "and the truth is my companion and I need some amends."

Philemon noticed that the strangers were oddly dressed, and that the younger had a staff of olive wood with a pair of wings near the top. He also thought the entwined snakes carved on it twisted and wriggled, but then his eyes were getting weak, so he might be mistaken.

As Philemon asked them to be seated, he thought he saw the staff go by itself to lean against the wall, but at once the elder asked, "Was there not in ancient times a lake covering the place where the village stands?"

"Not in my day, nor in my father's," said Philemon, "and doubtless it will be the same when I am gone."

"That is more than can be foretold," said the stranger. "Since the inhabitants have forgotten the affections and sympathies of their nature, it were better the lake should ripple over the village again." He looked very stern and as he shook his head, there was a roll of thunder in the air.

After visiting pleasantly for a while, the two travelers asked Philemon to express a wish. He said that both he and his wife wished that they should die, as they had lived, together. "You are a good man," said the elder, "and you have a good wife. It is fit your wish be granted."

The supper was then ready but Baucis made apologies for the poor fare. "Had we known you were coming, my good man and I would have gone without."

"Do not trouble yourselves," said the elder, "for a hearty welcome works wonders with poor fare." And they began to eat.

There was bread and cheese, and honey, and milk in a pitcher. Then a strange thing happened. The staff hopped up the steps and into the room and stood beside the younger man whose name, so he said, was Quicksilver. Both men ate heartily and drank all the milk in their bowls at a draught. "A little more milk, kind mother Baucis," said Quicksilver.

"Oh I am so sorry," she said. "The truth is that there is no more milk."

"Why it appears to me" said the traveler, "that there is more milk." And so saying he poured both bowls full. Baucis couldn't believe her eyes. Again Quicksilver asked for more milk. She took the pitcher and made a gesture without the remotest idea that the milk would stream forth. To her surprise it flowed, and the stale bread was soft, and the honey was fit for the gods. Baucis whispered to her husband that she thought this was a dream. "But say what you will, these are uncommon people," she said.

Philemon bestirred himself and took the pitcher to see if the marvel was real. He peeped in. It was empty but all at once the milk gushed up till it was full.

"Who are you, wonder-working strangers," cried Philemon.

"Your guests, good people, and may your pitcher never be empty."

The supper over, the strangers were shown to their room. Since there was only one bed, the old couple slept on the floor. Next morning Baucis made preparation for breakfast but the strangers were eager to be on their way, so the old couple walked with them a short distance to show them the road they were to take.

"Well a day," said Philemon, "if our neighbors only knew what a blessed thing it is to show hospitality to strangers, they would tie up the dogs and never allow children to throw another stone."

"I mean to go this day to tell them what naughty people they are," said Baucis.

"I fear," remarked Quicksilver, "that you will find none of them at home."

"When men do not feel toward the humblest stranger as if he were a brother," said the traveler in tones so deep that they sounded like those of an organ, "they are unworthy to exist on earth, which was created as the abode of a great human brotherhood. And by the bye, my dear people, where is this same village you talk about?"

The old couple turned toward the valley where the village had been, and saw only the broad blue surface of a lake, as tranquil as if it had been there since time began.

"Alas, what has become of our poor neighbors?" said Baucis.

"They no longer exist as men and women," said the elder. "There was neither use nor beauty in their lives. But you with your scanty means have mingled so much hospitality with your entertainment that milk became an inexhaustible fount of nectar, and bread and honey, ambrosia." So the old couple received their wish to leave the world at the same instant, and when they turned to look at their cottage, it had become a marble palace. Then they wished to thank the men, but they had vanished completely.

So they lived in the palace a long time and did much good, but one morning they were gone. Their guests searched everywhere to no purpose. But after a while they saw two trees before the portal that hadn't been there before. The boughs were entwined as if they embraced one another. When a breeze came up, the oak said "I am Philemon," and the linden said "I am Baucis," and the sound of the leaves seemed to say "Welcome!"

Note: Baucis (bô´sis) and Philemon (filē´mon) two mythological characters were rewarded for their kindness to Zeus and Hermes who were traveling in disguise. There are many versions of this ancient myth, the theme of which is the same as that of many other stories, - not what we have but what we share.

16

The Golden Touch

Adapted from *The Golden Touch*, by Nathanial Hawthorne, taken from Ovid, (43 B.C.—14 A.D.).

A very rich king named Midas had a beautiful daughter who was called Marygold. Now Midas was very fond of gold. The only thing he loved more was his daughter, but the more he loved her, the more he desired wealth. Before he possessed this insane desire for riches, he had shown a great taste for flowers, and he still had a beautiful garden. But now he kept wondering how much the roses would be worth if the petals were of gold. He spent more and more time in his treasure room counting his riches.

One day while he was counting gold, he saw a shadow fall over the table, and on looking up suddenly, he saw a stranger in a narrow sunbeam. "He must be more than mortal," Midas thought, "because I locked all the doors." So he was sure the stranger came to do him a favor.

"You are a wealthy man, friend Midas," observed the man. "I doubt any four walls contain so much gold as you have piled up in this room."

"Oh, I've done pretty well," said Midas, "but after all it is only a trifle considering that I have spent my whole life to get it."

"What!" exclaimed the stranger, "Then you are not satisfied?"

Midas shook his head.

"And pray what would satisfy you?" asked the visitor. "Merely for the curiosity of the thing, I should like to know."

The King thought and thought and finally he looked the stranger in the face.

"Well, Midas," observed the visitor. "I see you have hit upon something. Tell me your wish."

"It is only this," replied Midas. "I'm tired of collecting my treasures with so much trouble. I wish everything I touch to be changed to gold."

"The Golden Touch," said he. "Are you sure it will satisfy you and will you never regret possession of it?"

"I ask nothing else to render me perfectly happy."

"As you wish," said the stranger waving farewell. "Tomorrow at sunrise you'll find yourself gifted with the Golden Touch."

As the first sunbeam of morning shone through the window, he was astonished to see the covering on the bed turn to gold. He sprang up to pull aside the window curtain. The tassel of the cord turned to gold. As he dressed, his clothes became soft gold cloth. He touched a book and it became a bundle of thin golden leaves. But when he put on his spectacles, he couldn't see through them, for the glass had turned to gold. That was a bit startling.

"Well," said he, "it is no great matter. We can't expect great good without some small inconvenience. My own eyes will serve for ordinary purposes, and little Marygold will soon be old enough to read to me." So he went down stairs smiling as he noticed the balustrade turn to gold, and the door-latch too, as he passed into the garden. He hardly noticed the fragrance of the roses, he was so intent on turning the petals to gold. Then after a brisk walk he had an excellent appetite for breakfast.

Just what the breakfast was it is hard to say but it surely was fit for a king. And then there was a bowl of bread and milk for his little daughter. He was waiting for her when he heard her sobbing, so hoping to put her in better spirits with a surprise, he touched the breakfast bowl and turned it at once to gold.

"How now, little lady," he said as she entered, "how is it with you this bright morning that you are so sad?"

She held out a golden rose. "Ah dear father, as soon as I was dressed I ran into the garden to gather roses for you, but they have all turned yellow and no longer have fragrance.

And then as she sat down she noticed the change in the china
bowl which had always been so colorful, but her disappoint-
ment was nothing compared to the King's as all his food
turned to gold. He was really terrified as the thought of
starving to death came to him. Marygold was aware of his
grief and wished to comfort him, so she ran to him and threw
her arms about his knees. He bent down and kissed her.
"My precious Marygold!" he said. But she did not answer.
She too had turned to gold. Now she really was worth her
weight in gold as the saying goes. His despair was great but
after some time had passed and he realized how wrong he had
been, the stranger appeared again.

"Well, friend Midas, how did you succeed with your
Golden Touch?" said he.

"I am very miserable," said Midas. "Gold is not
everything. I have lost all that my heart really cared for."

"Ah, so you have made a discovery. Which is better,
the gift of the Golden Touch or a cup of cold water?" said he.

"Oh blessed water," said Midas.

"The Golden Touch or a crust of bread?" said the
stranger.

"Oh a piece of bread is worth all the gold on earth!"

"The Golden Touch or your little daughter?"

"My poor child," cried Midas. "I would not have given
that one small dimple on her chin for changing the whole
earth to gold."

"You are wiser than you were," said the stranger.
"Now if you sincerely wish to rid yourself of the Golden
Touch, go and plunge yourself into the river that runs past
your house, and take this pitcher, fill it with that water, and
sprinkle it over any object you wish to change back." With
that the stranger vanished.

You may be sure Midas lost no time in doing what he
was told to do, but he was most happy to restore his daughter
to her own sweet self. Her hair, however, always kept that
golden color, and he often said in after years that he hated
the sight of gold, all except that golden hair.

*The theme of this ancient story is found again
and again in literature, and surely the opera Faust
will come to mind as one thinks of bargaining with
the devil or with supernatural beings.*

17

Sindbad
The Sailor

Adapted from *The Adventures of Sindbad the Sailor*, by Laurence Housman.

Sindbad had been living in peace and contentment in Baghdad for some time when a messenger came with a request from the caliph. He wished to send Sindbad to the King of Sarandib with a letter and a gift. It was of course, his duty to obey his master, so with a letter and a sum of money for expenses, he set forth.

The gift was one of great magnificence. First there was a splendid white horse, the equal of which was not to be found in the length and breadth of Arabia. Its saddle and trappings were adorned with gold and set with brilliant jewels. Then in addition to this there were a priceless robe fit for the king of all the earth; a great quantity of rich stuffs from Egypt and Greece; and a wonderful crystal goblet of great worth.

Sindbad took the gifts and set sail with a company of merchants. They journeyed for long days and nights until at length they came to the island of Sarandib. Sindbad went at once to the king in his palace, delivered the gifts and received a joyous welcome. It was with some difficulty that he obtained permission to depart, for his visit had been so much enjoyed, But finally he set sail, glad to go back to the quiet and uneventful life he had vowed to live.

Not many days on their course as they passed near an island, a fleet of boats put off from shore and surrounded them. They were manned by men clad in suits of mail. They looked like demons armed with swords and daggers. They slew those who resisted and took the rest prisoners. Then they towed the ship to shore and took all the merchandise. The prisoners were sold as slaves.

Fortunately for Sindbad, he was purchased by a rich man who treated him kindly. He was given light tasks around the house, and after a few days his master said, "Are you skilled in any art or trade?"

Sindbad answered, "I am a merchant and skilled in the art of buying and selling."

"Can you use a bow?" the master asked.

"Yes, I can," said Sindbad and to prove it he pierced a mark at fifty paces.

"It is well," said the master, "you are skilled." So next day he placed Sindbad behind him on an elephant and at nightfall they journeyed to a place where there were many high trees. Sindbad was ordered to climb a tree and sit there ready with his bow and arrows till the elephants came at dawn. If he was successful in shooting one, he was to report to the master at once.

A great many elephants came when the sun rose and finally Sindbad sent a well aimed shaft into the brain of one of the beasts killing him instantly. As soon as evening came and the elephants departed, Sindbad ran to tell his master who of course, rejoiced at the news.

Day after day this went on until one day a great herd of ferocious elephants came to the tree. The biggest one thundered around the tree and then wound his trunk around it and tore it from the ground. Sindbad was lying half stunned on the ground where he had fallen when the elephant seized him in his trunk, bore him aloft and then led the whole herd in a wild stampede that shook the earth. Nor did they stop till they came to a valley where there were great heaps of elephant bones, teeth and tusks. This was their burying ground. There the elephant set him down gently and departed.

When Sindbad looked about and saw the wealth of gleaming tusks, he said to himself, "The elephants did not like the death of one of their number everyday, and they have done this to show how I may come by an abundance of tusks without further slaughter. Then he went back to his master who welcomed him as if he had returned from the dead, for indeed when he found the tree torn up the master feared for the life of his slave. You may be sure they lost no time in getting back to the place where so much wealth was stored, and at the sight of all that ivory, the master's joy knew no bounds. Of course Sindbad was freed and rewarded with much money and merchandise. On the homeward journey he visited many cities and traded for great profit. When he reached home, the caliph was astonished and delighted with his exploits and commanded that the story be written in letters of gold. He also promised that he would never send him forth again but would allow him to remain at home to enjoy his great wealth.

Sindbad was a sailor who was noted for his fabulous wealth. The source of his riches was a mystery until he decided to hold seven receptions and at each, to relate one of his seven fantastic exploits. The above was the seventh adventure.

18

General Moulton and the Devil

Taken from *Myths and Legends of Our Own Land*, by Charles M. Skinner, Copyright 1896, J. P. Lippincott.

Jonathan Moulton of Hampton, Massachusetts, was a general of consequence in the colonial wars, but a man not always trusted in other than military matters. One evening he sat musing at his fireside on the hardness of life in new countries and the difficulty of getting wealth, for old Jonathon was fond of money, and the lack of it distressed him worse than a conscience.

"If only I could have gold," he muttered, "I'd sell my soul for it."

Whiz! came something down the chimney. The general was dazzled by a burst of sparks, from which stepped forth a lank personage in black velvet in clean ruffles and brave jewels. "Talk quick, general," said the unknown, "for in fifteen minutes I must be fifteen miles away in Portsmouth." And picking up a live coal in his fingers he looked at his watch by its light. "Come, you know me. Is it a bargain?"

The general was a little slow to recover his wits, but the word "bargain" put him on his mettle, and he began to think of advantageous terms.

"What proof may there be that you can do your part in the compact?" he inquired.

The unknown ran his fingers through his hair and a shower of guineas jingled on the floor. They were pretty warm, but Moulton, in his eagerness fell on hands and knees and gathered them to his breast.

"Give me some liquor," then demanded Satan, for of course he was no other, and filling a tankard with rum, he lighted it with a candle, remarked affably, "To our better acquaintance," and tossed off the blazing dram at a gulp. "I will make you," said he, "the richest man in the province. Sign this paper and on the first day of every month I will fill your boots with gold; but if you try any tricks with me you will repent it. For I know you, Jonathon. Sign."

Moulton hesitated. "Humph!" sneered his majesty. "You have put me to all this trouble for nothing." And he began to gather up the guineas that Moulton had placed on the table. This was more than the victim of his wiles could stand. He seized a pen that was held out to him, and trembled violently as a paper was placed before him; but when he found that his name was to appear with some of the most distinguished in the province his nerves grew steadier and he placed his autograph among those of the eminent company with a few crooked embellishments and all the t's crossed. "Good," exclaimed the devil, and wrapping his cloak about him he stepped into the fire and was up the chimney in a twinkling.

Shrewd Jonathon went out the next day and bought the biggest pair of jack-boots he could find in Hampton. He hung them on the crane on the last night of that and all the succeeding months so long as he lived, and on the next morning they brimmed with coins. Moulton rolled in riches. The neighbors regarded his sudden wealth with amazement, then with envy, but afterward with suspicion. All the same Jonathon was not getting rich fast enough to suit himself.

When the devil came to make a certain one of the periodical payments he poured guineas down the chimney for half an hour without seeming to fill the boots. Bushel after bushel of gold he emptied into those spacious money-bags without causing an overflow, and he finally descended to the fireplace to see why. Moulton had cut the soles from the boots and the floor was knee-deep in money. With a grin at the general's smartness, the devil disappeared, but in a few minutes a smell of sulphur pervaded the premises and the house burst into flames. Moulton escaped in his shirt, and tore his hair as he saw the fire crawl, serpent-like over the beams, and fantastic smoke-forms dance in the windows. Then a thought crossed his mind and he grew calm; his gold that was hidden in wainscot, cupboard, floor, and chest, would only melt and could be quarried out by the hundred weight, so that he could be well-to-do again. Before the ruins were cool, he was delving amid the rubbish, but not an ounce of gold could he discover. Every bit of his wealth had disappeared. It was not long after that the general died, and to quiet some rumors of disturbance in the graveyard, his coffin was dug up. It was empty.

This is a tale from Puritan Land during colonial days. Notice the resemblance to other tales of bargaining with the Devil.

19

Legend of the Street of the Green Cross (Calle de la Cruze)

Taken from *Legends of the City of Mexico*, by Thomas A. Janvier, Copyright 1910, Harper and Brothers.

This Mexican legend is the joyful story of a gentleman and lady who loved each other, and were married, and lived in happiness until they died. It was because of this happiness that the gentleman caused to be carved on the corner of his house, this great green cross of stone that is still there.

It was a fine house in the days when Donna Maria's father built it. Now it is old and shabby and the saint that once stood in the niche above the cross is gone. But there is an excellent restaurant there - it is called the Heroina- where pulque of the best and the freshest is to be had every morning of every day the whole year round.

It is told that this gentleman, who was named Don Alvaro Manrique, came to Mexico in the train of the Viceroy Peralto - so it must have happened a long time ago.

This Don Alvaro was a very handsome man - tall, and slender, and fair; and he wore clothes of white velvet worked with white gold, and a blue cap with a white feather; and he rode always a very beautiful Arabian horse. His hair and his little pointed beard were a golden brown; and he was a sight to behold.

It happened one day that he was taking the air on his Arabian; and he was wearing - because a festival of some sort was in

progress - all of his fine clothes. So he came prancing down
the street, and in the balcony of that corner house - the house
on which the green cross now is - he saw a very beautiful
young lady, who was most genteel in her appearance, and as
white as snow. He fell in love with her on that very instant;
and she - although because of her virtue and good training she
did not show it - on that very instant she fell in love with him.
Then he made inquiry and found that her name was Dona
Maria Segura. Therefore he resolved to marry her. And so
every day he rode past her balcony and looked up at her with
eyes full of love. As for Dona Maria, she was so well
brought up and her parents watched her so carefully, that it
was a long time before she made any answering sign. And
for that reason she loved him all the more tenderly in her
heart.

Then it happened at the end of a long while that Dona
Maria's mother fell ill and so the watch upon her was less
close. Don Alvaro was then able to get into her hands a
letter in which he begged that she would give to him her love.
And he told her in his letter that if she could not answer it
with another letter, she should give him one of two signs by
which he would know her will. If she did not love him, she
was to hang upon the railing of her balcony a cross of dry
palm leaves, and when he saw that dry cross, that day he
would most certainly die. But if she did love him, she was
to hang a cross of green palm leaves upon the railing of her
balcony, and when he saw that he would know that she had
given him her true promise of heaven perfect happiness for
all his life long.

Being a lady, Dona Maria let some days go by before
she hung on her railing any cross at all, and during those
days Don Alvaro was no more than a hair's breadth of going
mad. And then on a day of days, when the spring-time sun
was shining and all the birds were singing love songs
together, Don Alvaro saw hanging on the railing of Dona
Maria's balcony a beautiful bright green cross!

Of course after that things went fast and well. By the
respectable intervention of a cleric, who was a friend of Don
Alvaro, and also a friend of Dona Maria's parents, all the
difficulties were cleared away in a hurry; and only a fortnight

after the green cross was hung on the railing of the balcony,
they went together to the altar, and at the foot of it they
vowed to each other their love. And what is best of all is that
they kept faithfully their vow.

Then it was, being gladly married, that Don Alvaro
caused the green cross of stone - so big that it rises to the
first floor from the pavement - to be carved on the corner of
the house that thence forth they lived in; and it was carved
beneath the very balcony where they had hung the green cross
of palm leaves that had given to him Dona Maria's true
promise of happiness for all his life long.

And there the cross still is and the name of the street
is the Calle de la Cruz Verde - which of course proves that
this story is true.

*pulque (pronounced pool ka) is a fermented
Mexican drink.*

*The Spanish word Calle meaning street is
pronounced as if it were spelled kai' ya.*

*A note to this legend explains that a bronze
tablet seen in the church of San Miguel, bore the
inscription "Dona Maria Manrique Aug. 11, 1573."
Don Alvaro Manrique came with the Viceroy in 1566,
so they must have been married only seven years.
Many streets in Mexico have unusual names and
these legends suggest that tragic facts colored by
superstition and imagination were the reason for
them. For example: The street of the Parade
where, they say, the skeletons walked for years;
The Alley of the Armed One, because a rich man
who lived there once always wore armor even as
a ghost.*

20

Paul
Bunyan

People in Maine say that Paul was born there, and was put out in the Atlantic Ocean in a floating cradle that set up such a tide with its rocking that it has not subsided to this day. But he was a full grown man by the time he came to the Minnesota lumber camp. Although everyone has heard about him, it has been impossible to find anyone who really saw him. Anyway, the statue of him on the shore of the lake at Bemidji, Minnesota, seems to represent fairly well, the picture in our minds. He was a really big man. With him we always associate Babe, his Big Blue Ox, usually described as being seven axe handles and a plug of tobacco wide between the eyes, and certainly he was big and powerful and a great asset to Paul. People say he was a blue ox because he was born the winter of the blue snow and his color was a sort of birth mark.

Now, Paul never bothered to snake one log at a time through the woods because with Babe he could snake great piles of them to a landing on a river at one time. Old Brimstone Bill made him a buckskin harness. Now, everybody knows that buckskin stretches when it is wet. Paul made good use of that fact in rainy weather. He would hitch Babe to a pile of logs and the harness would stretch so much that Babe could travel clean to the landing and the load wouldn't move from the skidway in the woods. Then he would fasten the harness with an anchor, and when the sun came out and the harness shrank, the load would be pulled to the landing while Paul and his ox were busy at some other job. They also tell that Paul used the Blue Ox to pull kinks out of crooked roads and to straighten rivers. Babe was full of tricks too. Sometimes he would sneak up behind a drive and drink all the water out of the river, leaving the logs high and dry. And for just a little snack, he'd eat fifty bales of hay, wire and all. Once Babe ran away and was gone all day roaming all over northern Minnesota and Wisconsin. His tracks were so far apart that it was hard to follow him and so deep that if a man fell in, it was very difficult for him to get out. They say that one settler and his wife and baby fell into one of those tracks and the son got out when he was fifty-seven years old and reported the accident. People say that those tracks filled up with water and that's how the ten thousand lakes were formed.

That happened after the winter of the deep snow. It was so cold that year that Lake Superior froze over clear to the bottom, and the snow was so deep that even the tops of the trees were buried. Food for the Blue Ox was scarce but Paul put green goggles on him and fitted him with snowshoes and so Babe went out and grazed on the snow and got along all right. In the spring Paul was afraid that Lake Superior wouldn't thaw out, so he cut huge chunks of ice and had Babe pull them up on shore so the sun could get at them and melt them. That winter it was so cold that one day the coffee pot in Paul's camp froze while it was boiling on the stove and the ice was still hot when it thawed out. The shadow of the Great Northern Depot at Fargo froze to the ground that winter and they say it is still there. When the snow packed down on the logging roads, it took longer than usual to melt it, so late in the spring that year, logs were hauled on ice roads that stood ten feet in the air.

Paul was always improving his methods of lumbering so by the time he was ready to log off North Dakota he had developed a system of hauling a section of land at a time to the landings. With that method there were no stumps left as anyone visiting North Dakota today can easily see. And so he finished his work in this part of the country and moved on out West. But with so many motels and parks and products named for him he won't soon be forgotten in these parts.

For generations the great American myth of Paul Bunyan has been known to the men of the lumbering industry and told around their camps, but it was the scholars of the 70's and 80's who recognized the importance of a written record of this myth, so at present libraries everywhere contain books and stories about Paul's exploits.

If you haven't heard all the stories about Paul Bunyan from your uncles and your grandfather, maybe you will want to go to the library and read some of the books to find out what all those professors had to say about him.

21

Rent Day

Taken from *Legends and Tales of Ireland*, by Lover (1797-1868) and Croker (1798-1854), published in London.

Bill Doody muttered as he sat on a rock by the Lake of Killarney. "What will we do? Tomorrow's rent day and Tim the Driver swears if we don't pay up our rent, he'll take everything we have; and then sure enough, there's Judy and myself and the poor children will be turned out to starve on the high road, for never a half penny of rent have I! Oh, that I should live to see the day!"

Thus did Bill Doody bemoan his hard fate, yet he was not so desolate as he supposed; there was one listening to him he little thought of, and help was at hand from a quarter he could not have expected.

"What's the matter with you, my good man?" said a tall portly-looking gentleman, as he stepped out of a furze-brake. Now Bill was seated on a rock that commanded a view of a large field. Nothing in the field could be concealed from him except this furze-brake, which grew in a hollow near the margin of the lake. He was therefore surprised at the gentleman's appearance and began to question if he belonged to this world or not. Soon, however he mustered courage to tell him how his crops had failed, how some bad spirit had charmed away his butter, and how Tim the Driver threatened to turn him off the farm if he didn't pay all his rent by twelve o'clock the next day.

"A sad story indeed," said the stranger; but if you tell your landlord agent, he won't have the heart to turn you out."

"Heart, your honor! said Bill. "I see you don't know him; besides he has had his eye on this farm, so I expect no mercy at all, only to be turned out."

"Take this, my poor fellow, take this," said the stranger, pouring a purse full of gold into Bill's old hat. "Pay the fellow his rent and I shall see that it does him no good."

Bill stared at the gold, but before he could look up to thank the man, he was gone. He thought he saw him riding a white horse a long way off on the lake.

"Oh, the blessed saints," shouted Bill, and he ran like madman to show Judy and to rejoice her heart with the prospects of wealth and happiness.

The next day Bill proceeded to the agent's, not sneakingly with his hat in his hand, but bold and upright like a man conscious of his independence.

"Why don't you take off your hat, fellow. Don't you know you are speaking to a magistrate?" said the agent.

"I know I'm not speaking to the King, sir," said Bill, "and I never takes off my hat but to them that I can respect and love. The Eye that sees all knows that I have no right to love or respect an agent."

"You scoundrel," said the agent, "I'll teach you to be insolent. But come, have you got the money for me? This is rent day. If there's one penny wanting you'll be turned out before night."

"There's your rent," said Bill with an unmoved expression, "you'd better count it, and give me a receipt in full."

The agent gave a look of amazement at the gold; for it was real. However willing the agent may have been to ruin the unfortunate tenant, he took up the gold, and handed the receipt to Bill who strutted off with it as proud as a cat is of her whiskers.

The agent going to his desk shortly after, was confounded at beholding a heap of gingerbread-cakes instead of the money he had deposited there. He raved and swore but all to no purpose; the gold had become gingerbread -

cakes just marked like the guineas, with the King's head, and Bill had the receipt in his pocket; so he saw there was no use in saying anything about the affair, as he would only get laughed at for his pains.

From that hour Bill Doody grew rich; all his under-takings prospered; and he often blesses the day he met with O'Donoghue, the great prince that lives down under the Lake of Killarney.

22

The Sun Fire at Sault Sainte Marie

Taken from *Myths and Legends of Our Own Land,* by C. M. Skinner, Copyright 1896, J. P. Lippincott.

Father Marquette reached Sault Sainte Marie, in company with Greysolon DuLhut, in August 1670 and was received in a friendly manner by the Chippewas. They however, warned him to turn back for the Ojibways beyond were notoriously hostile to the Europeans. But Marquette refused to change his plans, and even ventured the assertion that he could tame White Otter, the Ojibway chief, and bring him to the cross. At dawn he and his henchmen set off in a canoe, but on arriving at White Otter's camp and speaking their errand, they were seized and bound to await death on the morrow. The wife of the chief asked mercy for the white men, but to no avail. The brute struck her to the ground. That night his daughter, Wanena, who had seen DuLhut at the trading post, and had felt the stir of a generous sentiment toward him, appeared before the prisoners when the camp was asleep, cut their bonds, led them to a canoe, and guided them to the Holy Isle. This was where the Ojibways came to lay their offerings before their God, Manitou, whose home was there. There the friendly red men would be sure to find them and rescue them, she thought.

There in a secluded glen stood the figure of Manitou, rudely carved from a pine trunk, six feet high, and tricked out with gewgaws. As they stood there, they heard steps and before they could conceal themselves, White Otter and eight of his men were upon them. DuLhut grasped a club from among the offerings that were strewed at the statue's feet and prepared to defend himself. The priest drew forth his crucifix and prayed. The girl dropped to the ground, drew the blanket over her head, and began to sing her death song.

"So the black-coat and the woman-stealer have come to die before the Indian's God?" sneered the chief.

"If it be God's will, we will die defying your god and you," replied Marquette. "Yet we fear not death, and if God willed, he could deliver us as easily as he could destroy that image." He spoke in an undertone to DuLhut, and continued confidently. "I challenge your God to withstand mine. I shall pray my God to send his fire from the sky, and burn this thing. If he does so, will you set us free and become a Christian?"

"I will; but if you fail you will die."

"And if I win, you must pardon your daughter."

White Otter grunted his assent.

The sun was high and brought spicy odors from the wood. Raising his crucifix with a commanding gesture, the priest strode close to the effigy, and in a loud voice cried in Chippewa, "In the name of God, I command fire to destroy this idol!"

A spot of light danced upon the breast of the image. It grew dazzling bright and steady. Then a smoke began to curl from the dry grass and feathers it was decked with. The Indians fell back in amazement, and when a faint breeze passed, fanning the sparks into flame, they fell on their faces, trembling with apprehension, for Marquette declared, "As my God treats this idol, so can he treat you!"

Then looking up to see the Manitou in flames, White Otter exclaimed, "The white man's god has won. Spare us, Oh mighty medicine!"

"I will do so if you promise to become as white men in faith and be baptized." Tamed by fear, the red men laid aside their weapons, and knelt at a brook where Marquette gave the rite of baptism to each. Wanena who had fainted from fright when she saw the idol burning, was restored, and it may be added that the priest who Christianized her

also married her to DuLhut, who prospered and also left his
name to a great city at the head of the lake. News of the
triumph of the white man's God went far and wide, and
Marquette found his mission easier after that. DuLhut alone
of those present was in the father's secret. He had
perpetrated a pious fraud, justified by the results as well as
by his peril. A burning glass had been fastened to the
crucifix and with that he had destroyed the idol.

23

The Ark on Superstition Mountains

Taken from *Myths and Legends of Our Own Land,* by C. M. Skinner, Copyright 1896, J. P. Lippincott.

The Pima Indians of Arizona say that the father of all men and animals was the butterfly, Cherwit Make (earth-maker) who fluttered down from the clouds to the Blue Cliffs at the junction of the Verde and Salt Rivers, and from his own sweat made men. As the people multiplied, they grew selfish and quarrelsome, so that Cherwit Make was disgusted with his handiwork and resolved to drown them all. But first he told them in the voice of the Northwind to be honest and to live at peace. The prophet Suha who interpreted this voice, was called a fool for listening to the wind, but next night came the East wind and repeated the command with an added threat that the ruler of heaven would destroy them all if they did not reform.

Again they scoffed and the next night the West wind cautioned them. But this third warning was equally futile. On the fourth night came the South wind. It breathed into Suha's ear that he alone had been good and should be saved, and bade him make a hollow ball of spruce gum in which he might float while the deluge lasted. Suha and his wife immediately set out to gather the gum which they melted and shaped until they had made a large rounded ark, which they ballasted with jars of nuts, acorn-meal, and water, and meat of bear and venison.

On the day assigned Suha and his wife were looking down

regretfully into the green valleys from the ledge where the
ark rested, when a hand of fire was thrust from a cloud and
it smote the Blue Cliffs with a thunder-clang. It was the
signal. Swift came the clouds from all directions and down
came the rain. Withdrawing into their waxen ball, Suha and
his wife closed the portal. Then for some days they were
rolled and tossed on an ever-deepening sea. Their stores
had almost given out when the ark stopped, and breaking a
hole in its side, the occupants stepped forth.

There was a tuna cactus growing at their feet, and they
ate of its red fruit greedily, but all around them was naught
but water. When night came on they retired to the ark and
slept - a night, a month, a year, maybe a century, for when
they awoke the water was gone, the vales were filled with
verdure, and bird songs rang through the woods. The
delighted couple descended the Superstition Mountains on
which the ark had rested, and went into its valleys where they
lived for a thousand years, and became the parents of a great
tribe.

But the evil was not all gone. There was one Hauk, a
devil of the mountains, who stole their daughters and slew
their sons. One day while the women were spinning flax and
cactus fibre, and the men were gathering maize, Hauk
descended into the settlement and stole another one of Suha's
daughters. The father whose patience had been taxed to the
limit, made a vow to slay that devil. He watched to see by
what way he had entered the valley. He silently followed him
into Superstition Mountains; he drugged the cactus wine that
his daughter was to serve him; then, when he had drunk it,
Suha emerged from his place of hiding and beat out the brains
of the stupified fiend.

Some of the devil's brains were scattered and became
seed for other evil, but there was less wickedness in the
world after Hauk had been disposed of then there had been
before. Suha taught his people to build adobe houses, to dig
with shovels, to irrigate their land, to weave cloth and to
avoid wars. But on his death-bed he foretold to them that
they would grow arrogant with wealth, covetous of the lands
of others, and would wage wars for gain. When that time
came there would be another flood and not one should be saved

- the bad should vanish and the good would leave the earth and live in the sun. So firmly do the Pimas rely on this prophecy that they will not cross Superstition Mountains, for there sits Cherwit Make - awaiting the culmination of their wickedness to let loose on the earth a mighty sea that lies dammed behind the range.

The Superstition Mountains are near Phoenix, Arizona.

24

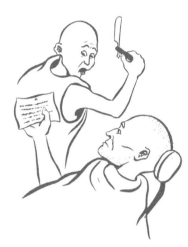

The Brahman's Verse

Taken from *Bengali Household Tales*, by William McCulloh, printed in London, 1912.

In a certain village there lived a very poor and ignorant Brahman. He had the greatest difficulty in getting a living. Indeed, so completely from hand to mouth did he live, that on any day that he failed to obtain alms, he had to fast altogether, and as if such a fortune were not sufficiently hard to bear, he had a wife whose tongue made him dread even to enter the house. What with this trial and his poverty together, the poor man was quite at a loss what to do or where to turn. Day and night the virago kept harping, "Just see how many Brahman pundits go to the Raja's house, recite a verse or two, and are rewarded with money enough to keep their wives and children in comfort, while you, like the utter good-for-nothing that you are, sit idling in the house, or when you do go begging, bring in the most wretched pittance. There are hundreds of ways of mending our fortunes, but you don't see them because you don't wish to."

"What ways?" answered the Brahman. "I'm quite uneducated myself. How then am I to compose a verse? And I'm not well acquainted with any pundit. So how am I to get a verse from somebody else, which I may pass off as my own?"

"Very well," cried the wife, snatching up her broom. "if you can do nothing, clear out!"

The poor Brahman made off, but once out, where was he to go? He could think of no place of refuge, so for a long time, he walked on without caring whither. At length he came to a large garden, and there sat down at the foot of a tree. As he sat he kept racking his brains how to improve his condition, but no possible way could he think of. In the midst of his ponderings, a pig happened to come to that place, and as pigs usually do, began to flounder in the water and then come up and rub her body against the tree, time and time again. For a while the Brahman watched her in silence. Suddenly a brilliant idea struck him, and he cried out, "I have it! I've made a verse at last." So saying he rose up and got a palm leaf, and wrote:

"Rubbing, rubbing, dipping, then rubbing with might and main;
What your rubbing's all for, is easy enough to explain!"

When he had written this, the Brahman said to himself, "Now shall I go to the Raja and recite my verse, and see what Destiny has in store for me? Why not? Who knows what he mayn't give me as a reward?" Having come to this decision, he set off at once.

It was evening when he reached the palace; the time of audience was over for that day, and the Raja had retired to the Rani's apartments. His attendants too had all gone off to their own quarters, so the Brahman could find no one to tell his errand to. As he waited he began to get rather nervous. "Likely enough when the Raja hears my verse, he will order me a beating instead of giving me a present," he thought to himself. "I'll run no such risks. I'll just leave it somewhere, and see what comes of it." Accordingly he sought out the place where the Raja was in the habit of sitting when he was getting shaved, and there he hung up the palm leaf with the verse on it, and hurried home. It was late when he arrived, and his wife began abusing him as usual, but he said, "What are you scolding about now? I've written a verse and left it at the palace. Just wait and see. Tomorrow you'll be made a Rani."

"Oh stop your jokes. Nobody here wants them. But that is just like you - an empty stomach and a head stuffed with nonsense."

"I'm perfectly serious," he said. "I did write a verse, and left it at the Raja's. I couldn't see him today, but tomorrow he can't fail to notice my verse. And won't he be delighted with it! We shall have no more trouble after that."

Next morning the Raja got up, washed his hands and face, and went to the place where he was used to sit when he was shaved. The barber was already there, strapping his razor.

Now the Rani and the Kotwal had plotted together to murder the Raja, but nobody had the courage to attack him openly. So at length the Rani sent secretly for the barber and said to him, "Tomorrow when you shave the Raja cut his throat with your razor. You shall receive an immense reward and incur no danger whatever." Well the hope of reward was too much for the barber so he promised to do this, and so this morning was making his razor very sharp. He was rubbing it on the whetstone, and dipping it in water, and rubbing it again and again. The Raja sat silently waiting, when suddenly his eye fell on the Brahman's verse, and quite without thinking, he read out loud:

"Rubbing, rubbing, dipping, then rubbing with might and main;
What your rubbing's all for, is easy enough to explain."

Hearing these words the barber was thunderstruck. He stared for a moment, then threw away his razor, strop and all, and fell at the Raja's feet, weeping bitterly, and cried "Maharaja, pardon me! I know nothing about it. It was the Rani and the Kotwal bade me. Maharaja, you would not kill a poor man like me." He was too frightened to say more. The Raja was astounded and said, "What is the matter? No harm shall come to you."

The barber said, "All I know is that yesterday her Majesty sent for me and said, 'Tomorrow when you are shaving the Raja, if you can manage to cut his throat, I will give you a big reward and promise that no harm shall happen to you!' The Kotwal said the same thing for he was there too. I was enticed by the bribe and intended to commit the crime, but you have detected all. Pardon me, your Majesty."

The Raja sent the barber away and proclaimed through the city that the maker of the verse should be seized and brought before him. The Brahman was of course alarmed and was sure he would lose his head. When the messengers laid hold of him, he said to his wife, "Nothing would suit you, but that I should go to the palace, and now see what has come of it." But she said, "What are you weeping for? You have done no wrong. Go along and see what Fate has in store for us." So weeping bitterly he was brought to the palace.

When he saw him, the Raja said, "Did you write this verse?" Still weeping, the Brahman said, "Yes, Maharaja."

Then the Raja said, "You have saved my life. How can I reward you as you deserve? The half of my kingdom is yours." On hearing these words the poor Brahman was over-joyed. The Raja at once proceeded to make him a Raja with all due ceremony, and meanwhile messengers were sent to the Rani and the Kotwal with orders that they were to be beheaded. Thereafter the Raja together with the Brahman and his wife continued to live together in the greatest happiness and splendor.

Note: Shaving with the Hindu is an important religious duty. When some poor foolish Brahman happened to save a life, he was supposed to have supernatural power. Kotwal is the chief of police. Rani (rah-nee) is the Raja's wife, and a sort of queen.

25

The Poor Man and the Rich Man

From *Grimms' Fairy Tales,* published in London. This story is included to show the similarity to the Baucis and Philemon tale which goes back to the time of Christ. This one comes from Germany at a much later date.

In olden times, when angels walked about the earth in the form of men, one of them while walking about saw night coming on and looked for shelter. He saw two houses opposite one!another, one large and handsome, the other miserably poor. Now the angel decided to lodge with the rich man because it would be easier for him to entertain a guest. Accordingly he knocked at the door, and the rich man opened it and asked what the stranger sought.

"I seek a night's lodging," said the angel.

The rich man noticed his ragged clothes and thought he did not have much money, so he shook his head and said, "I cannot take you in; my rooms are full of herbs and seeds, and if I were to shelter everyone who comes, I should soon be a beggar myself."

So he shut the door, and the angel immediately went to the house of the poor man. He scarcely had knocked when the door opened, and the poor man bade the stranger welcome, saying, "Stop here this night, here with me; it is too dark for you to go further."

The angel was pleased and walked in, and the wife also extended her welcome, saying, "Make yourself at home; we haven't much, but what we have we give with all our hearts." Then she placed some potatoes on the fire, and while they were boiling, she milked her goat, so there would be milk to drink. When the meal was ready the good angel ate with them, and it tasted good because those who ate were happy. When it was bedtime, the wife called her husband aside, and said, "Let us sleep on the straw tonight, so this poor wanderer may have our bed, for he has walked all day and is very tired."

At first the good angel refused this offer, but at last he yielded and the good couple made a cot of straw on the ground. The next morning they arose and cooked a breakfast for their guest. After eating, he set out again, but at the doorway he paused and said, "Because you have been so compassionate and pious, you may wish three times and I will grant what you desire."

The poor man replied, "What better can I wish for in the first place than eternal happiness, and second, that we may have health and strength and our daily bread so long as we shall live. But I know not what to wish for in the third place."

"Why not wish for a new house in place of this old one?" said the angel.

"Oh yes, I should like that," said the man, "if I can keep it on this spot."

Then the good angel fulfilled his wishes changing the old house into a new one on the spot, and giving them once more his blessing, he went out of the house.

When the rich man arose, and looked out of his window, he saw a handsome new house of red brick where the old hut had stood. Calling his wife he said, "Tell me what has happened; only yesterday there was a miserable old hut standing opposite, and today there is a fine new house! Run out and hear how this has happened!"

So the wife went and asked the poor couple and heard the story of the stranger. They told how a wanderer had come the night before, seeking a night's lodging, and that when he left in the morning, he had granted them three wishes. So she ran home and told her rich husband, and he exclaimed, "Ah, had I only known it! The stranger came here first and would have staid with us had I not sent him away."

"Be quick then," said his wife, "mount your horse and overtake him and ask for three wishes for yourself." So he followed her advice and soon overtook the angel. He made apologies for turning him away and all sorts of excuses, and made the angel promise to stop on his return.   Then the rich man asked if he too might be granted three wishes.

The angel said, "Yes, but it will not be good for you, and it would be better if you did not wish."   But the rich man insisted, so the angel said, "Ride home, and your three wishes shall be granted."

On the way home, he thought very hard, and let loose the reins, so the horse began to jump about, and the rich man couldn't concentrate on his wish.

Patting his horse on the neck, he said, "Be quiet," but it only whisked more than ever so the man became angry and cried impatiently, "I wish you'd break your neck!"

No sooner had he said it, than down fell the horse and broke his neck.   Thus he had his first wish.   Not wanting to leave the saddle behind, he cut it off, slung it over his back and went home on foot.   "I still have two wishes," he thought to himself, and so was comforted.

The sun scorched him terribly as he passed over the sandy commons, and the saddle hurt his back.   He was vexed and angry.   He thought many times that he knew what to wish for, but it always seemed too small.   He suddenly thought how comfortable his wife was at that moment, sitting at home in her cool room, and it made him so angry that he said without thinking at all, "I wish she was sitting on this saddle and couldn't get off it, instead of my having it slipping about on my back."

No sooner had he said it, than the saddle disappeared from his back and now he had only one wish left.   So he began to run intending to lock himself in his room to consider something great for his last wish.   But when he reached the house, he found his wife sitting on the saddle in the middle of the room crying because she couldn't get off.

"Well," he said, "I'll wish for all the riches in the world, only sit there for a time."   But she said, "Of what use are all the riches in the world if I have to sit on this saddle forever?   You wished me on; now wish me off."

So the rich man had to utter his third wish, much against his will so his wife could be freed, and immediately she was.   Thus he gained nothing from his wishes but trouble, scolding, and a lost horse.   The poor couple on the other hand, lived contented and pious to the end of their lives.

26

The Wily Jackal

Taken from *Bengali Household Tales*, by William McCulloh, printed in London 1912, Hodder, and Stroughton.

Once on a time in a certain forest, a lion, a tiger, a mongoose, a mouse, and a jackal were living together on very friendly terms. One day the lion saw an elephant feeding. Thereupon he said to himself, "We must contrive to get that elephant to eat." and calling on the jackal, he told him that he must manage somehow to have the elephant killed. "As your majesty commands," he replied and went off in search of the mouse.

When he found him he said, "Brother, you've got to kill that elephant."

"I kill the elephant!" answered the mouse. "The elephant's a huge brute. How's a tiny creature like me going to kill him?"

"You can manage it this way," said the jackal. "Burrow a tunnel under the ground from where you are standing to the place where the elephant is feeding. When he sets his foot on the spot where the ground is hollowed out below, it'll give way. Then do you gnaw through the tendon of his foot with your teeth, and he'll fall down and soon die." The mouse burrowed a tunnel as the jackal bade him, and when the ground gave way under the elephant's foot, and it sank down into the hole, he bit through the tendon of the heel, and the elephant came down bodily with a great crash, , and in no long time, died.

The jackal now went back to the lion and said, "Master, your orders have been carried out. The elephant's dead." The lion was highly delighted at the news, and thought to himself what a fine feast all five of them would have. The jackal for his part thought to himself, "I've been clever enough to bring about the death of the elephant. Now I must show myself clever enough to get the whole of him for myself to eat." So he said to the lion, "Master, this is a most auspicious day. First bathe and perform the stated rites for the benefit of your deceased grandfather, and then come and regale yourself with the flesh of the elephant." The lion quite approved of this suggestion, and went off presently followed by the other three friends, to a neighboring tank to bathe, while the jackal remained on guard beside the carcass of the elephant.

The lion returned first from his bath. When he came up, the jackal said to him, "Master, I've something to say to you. Will it be safe for me to speak quite frankly?"

"By all means, speak frankly," was the reply.

"Well, Master," said the jackal, "the mouse has been saying to me, 'The lion is the king of all animals. He's in the habit of killing for himself and us too. Will he actually condescend to eat an animal that we have killed!'"

When he heard this the lion said, "That's quite true. I eat what I've killed myself. It's altogether beneath my dignity to eat an animal that the mouse has killed." So saying he walked off feeling more dignified than pleased. He had just gone when the tiger turned up. The jackal said to him, "For some reason or other the lion is in a great rage at you. He gave me orders to let him know as soon as you reappeared. I thought it only friendly to tell you about this. You will of course do as you think fit." The tiger thought to himself, "What's the use of quarrelling with the lion? He's a very powerful animal. It's wiser to forego the chance of a feed of elephant flesh than to risk a fight with him. I'll just take myself off for a while."

The mongoose came next. "What have you done to anger the tiger?" the jackal asked him forthwith. "I'm to inform him the moment you put in an appearance. And it's only fair to tell you that he looked as if he meant business, when he gave me the order. You'd better consider well what you ought to do under these circumstances."

"It's out of the question for me to think of quarrelling with the tiger," replied the mongoose. "He's a thousand times as big and strong as I am. The only course for me is to clear out." Which he did. Last of all, the mouse appeared. As soon as he saw him, the jackal said, "How have you fallen out with the mongoose? I'm to tell him the moment I see you. He seems to have some score to pay off. Anyway, I've told you. You know yourself what you had better do."

"I mustn't quarrel with him, whatever I do," answered the mouse. "Like enough he would prefer me to elephant. I had better be going." And he too, went off. Much elated by the success of his plan, the jackal now proceeded to dispose of the elephant.

Great "lion" nations dividing the spoils of war, as we now well know, have been trapped by jackal partners.

27

The Silent Wager

Taken from *Bengali Household Tales*, by William McCulloh, printed in London, 1912.

In a certain village dwelt a Brahman and his wife. One day the wife felt a very strong desire for fish. So she said to her husband, "Do get me some fish to eat."

"Very well, I will," he said, and going to the bazaar, he bought three, which he fetched home and gave to his wife. She cut them up, cleaned them and cooked them. When suppertime came, the Brahman said, "I will eat two of the three fish."

"No, you shan't," said she, "I'll eat two."

"What?" cried her husband. "Am I not your lord and master, a person to be regarded with the greatest reverence? It is only fit and proper that I should eat the two."

"Fudge!" said the wife, "I am only a servant, am I, that I should be content to get one?"

"Who went to the bazaar for them, I should like to know?" asked the Brahman.

"And who cooked them, I should like to know?" rejoined his wife.

"I am your husband whom you are bound to treat with deference and respect," said he. "Moreover, I took a deal of trouble to fetch these fish. So I must get two."

"And I am your wife," she answered, "to whom you are bound to be as kind as you can.

Moreover, I took no end of trouble to cook these fish nicely. I must get the two."

Neither would give way and the quarrel between them grew hotter and hotter. At length the Brahmani said, "Let us go to bed and see who speaks first. Whichever of us does, will have to take one fish." "That's a good idea," said the husband. Accordingly they lay down, leaving their supper - rice, fish, and what not - untouched. They passed the night in absolute silence; neither the one or the other would utter a syllable. Day dawned; the morning passed; it was getting on to noon: but they continued to lie perfectly still; neither one of them would so much as get up to open the house-door.

The neighbors began to wonder what had happened. One after another came and called the Brahman and his wife, but in vain. Again and again they shouted as loud as they could, but nobody answered. At length the people came to the conclusion that both of them must have died suddenly during the night. So they broke open the door and entering the house, began to call to them again. Still neither answered. They shook them and pulled them about; neither made the slightest sound. The neighbors being now quite sure that they were dead, carried them away to the burning-ghat, and leaving three of their number to perform the funeral rites, returned to their homes. The three who remained made up the pyre, placed the Brahman upon it, and applied the torch. Then they lifted up the Brahmani to lay her beside her husband. Just at that moment the flames reached the body of the Brahman. Unable to lie still or keep quiet any longer, he jumped up crying, "Wife, I'll eat the one". "Then I'll eat the other two," she promptly replied.

Instantly the three villagers, convinced that they had become Bhuts, (which were demons that were inhabited by corpses) and were speaking of devouring the three of them, dropped the Brahmani and ran for their lives. The Brahman and his wife followed them, he repeating "I will eat the one," and she saying, "I will eat the two." When they got to their own house, they had their supper for breakfast, the husband taking one fish and the wife the other two.

In modern days when husband and wife have an argument, the husband often says, "We compromise, and she gets her way."

There are several versions of the story of stubborn people who would rather die than give in. The Five Eggs from Ecuador is a familiar tale of the stubborn wife.

This story is added as a sort of garnish - an extra touch! It was obtained through the courtesy of Frank Rarig, Jr., of St. Paul, Minnesota. Frank Rarig, Sr., who was for many years head of the Speech Department at the University of Minnesota adds this interesting comment: "The late W. C. Coffey who was then President of the University, took a copy of this story to Washington, D.C. where he attended a meeting of the Farm Bureau, and showed it to some members who liked it so well that they had it put in the Congressional Record."

Lincoln's reputation as a storyteller is well known. No doubt he enjoyed this one as it seems to be known as Lincoln's "Jackass" Story.

From George Vane, Hamline University, comes this additional note: "Petroleum V. Nasby was the pseudonym of David Ross Locke (1833-1888), whose humorous pieces especially during the Civil War delighted the North and confounded the South. Abraham Lincoln so thoroughly enjoyed the semi-literate letters of the northern secessionist Nasby that he once declared that he would gladly give up the presidency for the genius to write the Nasby pieces."

28

Lincoln's "Jackass" Story

Wunce they was a king, who hired him a prophet to prophet him his weather. And one day the king notioned to go fishin' but the best fishin' place was nigh onto where his best gal lived. So he aimed to wear him his best clothes. So he called in his prophet and he says, "Prophet, is hit a comin' on to rain?" And the prophet says, "No, king, hit aint a comin' on to rain, not even a sizzle-sozzle." So the king he put on his best clothes and he got his fishin' tackle, and he started down the road towards the fishin' place and he met a farmer ridin' a jackass. And the farmer says, "King, if ye aint aimin' to get yore clothes wetted, ye'd best turn back for hit's a comin' on to rain, a trash-mover and a gulley-washer." But the king drewed himself up and he says, "Farmer, I hired me a high-wage prophet to prophet me my weather and he 'lows how hit hain't a comin' on to rain not even a frog-duster." So the king he went a fishin' and hit come on to rain, a clod-buster and a chunk-mover. And the king's clothes wuz wetted and they shrunked on him, and the king's best gal she seen him and laughed and the king was wroth and he went home and he throwed out his prophet and he says, "Farmer, I throwed out my other prophet and I aim to hire you to prophet me my weather from now on'ards." And the farmer says, "King I haint no prophet. All I done this evenin' was to look at my jackass' ears. For if hit's a comin' on to rain his ears lops down and the harder hit's comin' on the lower they lays, and this evenin' they was a layin' and a loppin'." And the king says, "Go home, farmer, I'll hire me the jackass." And that's how it happened. And the Jackasses have been a holdin' down all the high wage governmint jobs ever since!

Petroleum V. Nasby